Jos. v. Stoklasa

Beginnings:

Beginnings:

GENESIS AND MODERN SCIENCE

By

Charles Hauret

Translated and adapted from the
fourth French edition by

E. P. Emmans, O.P., S.T.Lr., S.S.Prolyta

Dubuque 1955

THE PRIORY PRESS

Revisores Ordinis:

       Joannes S. Considine, O.P., S.T.M.

       Richardus T. A. Murphy, O.P., S.T.P., S.T.D., S.S.I).

Imprimi potest:

       Eduardus L. Hughes, O.P., S.T.M.

                   Prior Provincialis

Nihil obstat:

       Richardus T. Murphy O.P., S.T.P., S.T.D., S.S.I).

                  Censor Librorum

Imprimatur

       ✠Leo Binz

                Archiepiscopus Dubuquensis

Die 5a Novembris, 1955

iv

Acknowledgement is made to the officials of the Confraternity of Christian Doctrine for permission to use the text of their version of the Bible; to the officials of the National Catholic Welfare Conference to use their translations of the papal encyclicals; to Longmans, Green and Co. for quotations from *Sacred History* by Daniel-Rops and *Human Destiny* by Lecomte du Nouy; to J. P. Kenedy and Sons for the quotation from the *Autobiography of St. Thérèse;* and to Fides for the quotation from *The Church Today* by Emmanuel Cardinal Suhard.

FOREWORD

The first three chapters of Genesis contain the divinely inspired account of human beginnings. It fascinates the lay as well as the scientific and religious mind; for in these chapters we are told of the creation of the world and of man, of a primitive state of happiness enjoyed by Adam and Eve, and of the sin which lost that happiness to themselves and their posterity—to us.

The story related in these chapters is accepted as true by all believers in God and in the Bible. But we cannot fail to notice that the age-old acceptance of this story by Jews, Catholics, and Christians in general, has recently been briskly challenged, especially by science. Minds shaped and formed by modern science experience great difficulties in understanding or reconciling the biblical account with the findings of science. That light was created before the sun; that creation took place in six days of twenty-four hours each; that the whole human race traces back to a single human couple; that all the evils in the world trace back to a conversation with a serpent, and to an original sin: these positions are adjudged difficult, if not impossible, to treat seriously.

But scholars are not the only ones interested in these things. The questioning minds of our youth, particularly those of a school age, want to known what reply they can return to modern questions. Does the Bible teach evolution? Is it opposed to evolution? Did Adam look like a Neanderthal man? How old is man, and the world? Teachers of religion want to know what to say to their pupils, and welcome a frank discussion of these points; nothing would please them more than thus to acquire answers which will arouse neither the derision of the unbeliever, nor the scorn of the well-informed.

If today a believing Christian merely repeats his belief in the Bible, he will be accused of being behind the times. His reason tells him that he must take cognizance of the accomplishments of science, and yet he feels—and rightly—that he must not fail to show respect for God's inspired word. Arrogant as science may sometimes be, one must render to it the things that are science's, never for a moment refusing God the things that are God's.

Between religion and true science there is no real conflict; there cannot be any. Science's task is to observe and correlate the laws implanted in nature by the Creator, and God's own laws cannot contradict him. The cosmos and the Book of Books, the Bible, both come from him, the Primal Truth who can *neither deceive nor be deceived. The cosmos does not contradict the Book; the Book does not contradict the cosmos; the one cannot contradict the other.*

Precisely here lies the value of M. Hauret's **Beginnings;** *it is a bridge between the principle just enunciated and the world of cosmic facts. The author, a priest-professor on the Theological Faculty of the University of Strasbourg, has courageously and honestly faced our modern difficulties; the fact that his book has met with a warm welcome in France, Spain and Italy is proof that it effectively meets an acute need. As an obedient son of the Church, he makes good use of the directives given by our Holy Father, Pope Pius XII, in his "Divino Afflante Spiritu" (1943) and "Humani Generis" (1950); he also follows the wise suggestions contained in the "Letter to Cardinal Suhard" (1948), by the then Secretary of the Pontifical Biblical Commission, Father James Vosté, O.P. These are all present-day documents; liberal, envisioning the future, opening wide the paths of research, they yet safeguard the tenets of the faith.*

It is deserving of note that the impetus to translate this work into English came from a priest-scientist, Monsignor Ulrich A. Hauber, long a professor of Biology at Saint Ambrose College in Davenport, Iowa, and past president of the Iowa Academy of Sciences. Through him Father Edward P. Emmans, O.P., sometime student under Père Lagrange at the Ecole Biblique of Jerusalem, was induced to make this translation.

Many of us cannot help but be aware of the difficulties experienced by some as they read the first pages of the Bible. It is well, therefore, that M. Hauret's work is now reaching an English speaking public. Doubtless in a field wherein so much is still a matter of controversy and scholars find much still to debate, some of today's opinions—conservative ones as well as liberal—may have one day to be revised or restated. Progress in this field is necessarily slow and largely depends on the discovery of new material. But the great strides which biblical studies have made during the past half century give reason to hope for continued progress: a progress which the Church motivates and guides. And love of the Church, the sole guardian and only safe interpreter of the Bible by divine commission, motivated and guided all who had a part in the publication of this book.

✝ EDWARD C. DALY, O.P., S.T.M.
BISHOP OF DES MOINES

TABLE OF CONTENTS

ABBREVIATIONS

A A S — Acta Apostolicae Sedis

A E R — American Ecclesiastical Review

A N E T — Ancient Near Eastern Texts (ed J B Pritchard)

C B Q — Catholic Biblical Quarterly

Cl R — Clergy Review

D A — Dictionnaire Apologétique

D T C — Dictionnaire de la Foi Catholique

E T L — Ephemerides Theologicae Lovanienses

H P R — Homiletic and Pastoral Review

Ir T Q — Irish Theological Quarterly

N Schol — New Scholasticism

N R T — Nouvelle Revue Théologique

P L — Patrologia Latina (Migne)

P G — Patrologia Graeca (Migne)

R B — Revue Biblique

R S R — Revue des Sciences Religieuses

Th Dig — Theological Digest

Th S — Theological Studies

V D B S — Vigouroux, Dictionnaire de la Bible, Supplément

INTRODUCTION

Believing Christians are often disturbed when they read the first chapters of the Bible. The narratives which enchanted them as children trouble and even scandalize them in their more mature years. Imbued as they are with the prevailing scepticism, disquieting comparisons come readily to their minds: the crafty serpent which talks and which deceives the mother of the human race, the wonderful plants of the Garden of Eden, the trees which give knowledge and immortality, all of these bring to mind *The Thousand and One Nights,* and fairy tales with their talking animals; and if they know something of the history of religions, their uneasiness increases. How can they forget that in the sacred books of the Egyptians and Sumerians and Assyrians there are tales similar to the biblical narratives?

1

If this is so, they ask, why give to one a credence which is rightly denied to the other?

The narratives of Genesis possess a wonderful candor, artlessness and simplicity. But does this recommend them? To have read the popular science magazines is to become aware of the overwhelming complexity of the origin of the universe and of man. In comparison with the learned explanations of the latter, the Bible makes us think of guileless children, ignorant of the complexities of life. The simplicity of the Bible is sometimes more offensive than attractive. Some sincere believers suffer from an inferiority-complex, even though they will not admit it; and some of them choose a rather radical solution, in order, they say, to save themselves from doubts against their faith: they decide to keep the holy book closed, to "put it on the Index." The tightly-sealed book will then no longer trouble their faith. But this is an evasion, not a solution. It is better not to run away from the difficulties, but to take a firm stand against them and so surmount them.

Even priests are not wholly spared these feelings of uneasiness. They know that the biblical narrative is not always to be taken exactly as the words sound; they know too that ingenious theories have been advanced to harmonize science and faith and to reconcile modern discoveries with the old narratives, but some of them cannot help but feel sceptical of the scholars. In the last hundred years how many restate-

2

ments and readjustments the scholars have had to make! Concordism* in particular has had its memorable ups and downs. These priests are aware that the general orientation is the same despite the transitory fluctuations, but their over-all impression is that in such matters much opportunism and arbitrariness prevails. This may perhaps be why they keep the problem of the beginnings of the universe and man out of their sermons, religious instruction classes, and discussion groups. If called upon for an explicit statement on this subject they become panicky and embark upon an explanation of the first chapters as if picking their way through a mined field where at every step they might find themselves blown sky high. To hear them talk, only specialists are sufficiently protected to pass safely through so many perils. And yet, is not a special knowledge of the word of God required of the ministers of the word?

Unbelievers smile sardonically at any attempt to discuss the biblical accounts of man's origin. Many of them have probably never read these accounts, and know of them only through distorted quotations, or in

---

*Concordism: an attempt to establish a strict harmony between the Scriptures and the positive sciences, especially geology, biology and anthropology, as if the Bible were some sort of master-blueprint of all science. Such attempts have all quite understandably foundered, for the Bible is not a science textbook. Was it not Galileo who said: "The Bible does not tell us how the heavens go, but how to go to heaven?"

snatches advanced in argument. Few indeed have undertaken a personal study of these questions.

* * * * *

And yet these texts, written under the inspiration of the Spirit of God, are the very breath of life for Christians, both learned and unlearned, and for this reason deserve the attention of all. These narratives are meeting-places and sometimes the battlegrounds for theologians and exegetes and scientists; they raise the perennial problems that command the attention of every thoughtful man. Despite their antiquity and strangeness of expression, they are very much alive, because they contain the answers to the profound questions asked by the men of our day.

"In the beginning God created heaven and earth . . . . These are the opening words of the Book of Books, and there is no theme of human invention that has served to fertilize the imagination to the same extent as have these first eleven chapters of Genesis. Christian morality has its source in them; the conceptions that millions of human beings have held and now hold of their destiny, the psychological explanation of our interior misery, the hope that sustains us, all that most clearly distinguishes us perhaps, comes from these pages."[1]

Exegetes of all schools have with ardor and curiosity delved deeply into these chapters. Filled with

4

difficulties they may be, but they are rich in doctrine. According to Saint Jerome, no Jew could begin the study of these texts before he was thirty years of age.[2] Much has been written on them; but simple, popular works on Genesis can almost be numbered on the fingers of one's hand.[3]

* * * * *

We are going to try to explain, without any attempt at erudition and from a practical point of view, the doctrinal content of the first three chapters of Genesis. After a few pages of introduction to the mysterious book which contains these chapters, we shall consider what the Bible says about the origin of the universe and man, and about primitive humanity. Read with Christian eyes, Genesis will be seen to be an outline of the pre-history of Christianity; it is the Gospel before the Gospels. We shall conclude our study with practical conclusions designed to fit catechetical teaching and preaching.

In the course of this study, the guardian of the sacred books and the pillar and wall of truth, the Church, will be our guide. We shall never lose sight of the fact that on several occasions ecclesiastical authority has intervened apropos of these chapters,[4] and at the proper time we shall interpret and apply these directives. We shall not hesitate to make use of the most recent writings of Catholic exegetes. If their explanations seem daring, we will not be too quick to censure them harshly. Rather let us meditate on the fatherly advice of our Holy Father Pius XII in his encyclical *Divino Afflante Spiritu:* "Let all the other sons of the Church bear in mind that the efforts of these resolute laborers in the vineyard of the Lord should be judged not only with equity and justice, but also with the greatest charity; all moreover should abhor that intemperate zeal that imagines that whatever is new should for that very reason be opposed or suspected. Let them bear in mind above all that in the rules and laws promulgated by the Church there is question of doctrine regarding faith and morals; and that in the immense matter contained in the Sacred Books—legislative, historical, sapiential, and prophetical—there are but few texts whose sense has been defined by the authority of the Church, nor are those more numerous about which the teaching of the Holy Fathers is unanimous. There remain, therefore, many things, and of the greatest importance, in the discussion and exposition of which the skill and genius of Catholic commentators may and ought to be freely exercised."[5]

Commenting on these very liberal directives, the Secretary of the Biblical Commission wrote to Cardinal Suhard: "This letter is only an application of the encyclical to two particular questions which trouble the minds of many, even of instructors in the primary schools."[6] One of these questions refers specifically to the historicity of the first chapters of Genesis.

* * * * *

These pages reproduce substantially a series of lectures on an advanced course in Religion. Though they have been re-written and enlarged, they still retain some trace of their original purpose.

Professional exegetes will learn nothing new from this study; indeed, they will find in it what is already theirs. Even so, we believe that what is said in these pages is an answer to the unspoken questions of many men and women of today.

NOTES

1 Daniel-Rops, *Sacred History* (N Y: Longmans, Green and Co, 1946) 62 f.

2 *Letter 53, to Paulinus; P L* 22: 547.

3 Work of a popular, semi-scientific nature on the problems of the opening chapters of Genesis are rather few in number; the following will prove useful to the readers of these pages: Msgr U A Hauber, "Evolution and Catholic Thought" *A E R* 106 (1952), 161-177; R T Murphy, OP, *The First Week—Theology for the Layman,* No 16 (Somerset, O: Rosary Press, 1952); R W Murray, *Man's Unknown Ancestors* (Bruce, 1943); D Donnelly, *The Bone and the Star* (S & W, 1944); T J Motherway, SJ, "Theological Opinion on the Evolution of Man," *Th S* 5 (1944) 198-221; Msgr Hauber, *Creation and Evolution*[3] (Paulist Press, NY, 1947); H J T Johnson, *The Bible and the Early History of Mankind* (B & O, 1947); Bruce Vawter, CM, *Does Science Prove the Bible Wrong?—K of C Pamphlet* No 48 (St. Louis, Mo, 1948); Alexander Jones, *Unless Some Man Show Me* (S & W, 1951); M J Gruenthaner, SJ, "Evolution and the Scriptures," *C B Q* 13 (1951), 21-27; N Luyten, O.P., "Philosophical Implications of Evolution," *N Schol* 23 (1951), 43-47; H F Davis, "Organic Evolution," *Cl R* 37 (1952), 21-27; L Dufault, "Philosophical and Biological Implications of Evolution," *American Cath Phil Publ* 26 (1952), 66-80; B Melendez, "Teleogenesis," *Th Dig* 1 (1953), 123-127; M A MacConaill, "The Evolutionary Dilemma," *Ir T Q* 20 (1953), 410-415; Margaret

Monro, *Thinking about Genesis* (Longmans, 1953); V Marcozzi, SJ, "The Origin of Man according to Science," *Th Dig* 2 (1954), 43-47.

Of a more scientific nature are M-J Lagrange, OP, *Historical Criticism and the O T* (CTS London, 1905); H Junker, *Die Biblische Urgeschichte . . .* (Bonn, 1932); F Ceuppens, OP, *Genèse I-III* (Desclée, 1945); *idem, Historia Primaeva-Genesis I-III²* (Marietti, 1947); E Messenger, *Theology and Evolution²* (Sands, 1952); J Chaine, *Le Livre de la Genèse* (Paris: Ed du Cerf, 1948); C Vollert, SJ, "Evolution of the Human Body," *Cath Mind* 50 (1952), 135-54.

For a detailed bibliography, cf F Ceuppens, O.P, *Hist Primaeva* and *R S P T* 38 (1949), 175-205; E. Arbez, "Genesis I-XI and Prehistory," *A E R* 123 (1950), 81-92, 202-213, 284-294.

4 By this is meant particularly the *responses* of the Biblical Commission dated June 27, 1906 and June 30, 1909. These will be interpreted in the light of the letter which J M Vosté, OP, Secretary of the Commission, addressed to Cardinal Suhard of Paris on Jan 16, 1949 (cf "The Pontifical Biblical Commission on the Pentateuch," *H P R* 48 [1948], 567-574), and of the encyclical *Humani Generis* of Pius XII, Aug 12, 1950 (N C W C, Wash, DC).

5 Pius XII, *Divino Afflante Spiritu*, September 30, 1943 (N C W C), 47.

6 J M Vosté, OP, "Lettre de la Commission Biblique," *Angelicum* 25 (1948), 164; cf *H P R, art cit,* 572.

CHAPTER ONE

The Bible, the Unknown

For many centuries the Bible was the textbook of religious and moral instruction. Today few people have any knowledge of the Bible, and many live in complete ignorance of it. Not so long ago Cardinal Mercier complained bitterly, "The New Testament ought to be the bedside book of every Christian who knows how to read. My heart bleeds because there are in my flock many Christians who have never read, who do not even have in their libraries—otherwise encumbered with a lot of worthless reading matter—the divine treasure which is the New Testament."[1] An even greater ignorance prevails concerning the Old Testament.

For the past several years, largely because of the liturgical revival, the faithful have begun to show an

11

increasing interest in the biblical portions of their missal. But for lack of instruction they sometimes become discouraged, and these fragments separated from their context often become insoluble puzzles for them.

It is impossible to instill a familiarity with the Bible in a few pages or to display all its treasures. Familiarity with it comes only from frequent and assiduous use, and the riches of this Book are as profound and inexhaustible as a bottomless sea. Our purpose is to make the Bible easier to approach and to facilitate contact with the *Unknown Book.*

How can this be done? It is really quite simple.

How do we ordinarily proceed to find out about another person? We begin by watching him. We note his facial characteristics, his build, his manner, his ideas, his language; we find out about his family and his place of birth. This preliminary inquiry gives us a superficial knowledge of him. But we must go beyond these external appearances and learn his personal tastes, his inner inclinations, likes and dislikes, his interests. In short, we have to get into his mind. This requires extended contact and serious conversation with him and a definite mutual attraction. Even then, it is only after a long time and at the cost of limitless patience that his character and personality come clearly into focus.

We shall adopt a similar procedure with regard to the Bible. A fascinating undertaking, not always successful, but always fruitful. And when we come to know this *Unknown,* we also shall love it.

I

Shall we begin with—pardon the expression!—the civil status of the Bible? With its passport-description? We shall carefully gather together all available information about it.

* * * * *

The *Unknown* bears a singular, unique name, evocative of an original nobility; it is called **The Book,** and *that* is actually the etymological meaning of the word "bible." The Bible is the book par excellence which takes precedence over all others, and indeed, supplants all competitors. This book is well named; its title rightfully belongs to it, and to it alone. Of this claim, more later.

Yet the title is a surprising one. As a matter of fact, the Bible comprises seventy-three books! It is a collection of books, not one book; it is a work in seventy-three volumes, a whole library gathered together into a single book.

The *Unknown* speaks several *languages;* it is a polyglot. Ordinarily it uses Hebrew, a language cognate to Arabic; forty-two of its books were written in it.[2] Sometimes it makes use of Aramaic, a language which soon rivalled, and finally supplanted, Hebrew. In all the countries of western Asia, Aramaic triumphed over the native languages and became the language of diplomacy and business. Three books, one of which is the Gospel according to Saint Matthew, were written in it.[3] Greek, that "sonorous language of masterly tones, the most beautiful that has ever come from human lips," is the language of the other parts of the Bible. With the one exception of Saint Matthew, the Gospels, Epistles, Acts and the Apocalypse were written in the popular Greek of ordinary conversation, but this Greek was not the classical language of Xenophon and Demosthenes.

Its *native land?* This is not an easy question to answer. We know with certainty that Moses, the great leader and genius versed in all the wisdom of the East and of Egypt, signed the birth certificate of the Bible. The Pentateuch, the first pages of which will be the subject matter of our study, is substantially the work of the Legislator of Israel. To him must be given the credit for a great part of its production; it was he who exercised a profound influence in its definitive redaction.[4]

The Book, therefore, came into being on the steppes of the Arabian peninsula in the 15th or 13th century B.C., depending on the date one assigns to Moses. With each succeeding book the Bible grew as a living thing, although it is not possible to affix a precise date to the different stages of its growth. It grew especially in Palestine, the "holy land" destined for so much glory. As it developed, the Book was so dependent on the history of the Jews that it underwent all the vicissitudes of the Jewish people, like a child who records in his subconsciousness all the crises of family life. When the Chosen People knew foreign invasion and deportation (587 B.C.), the Bible accompanied the exiles into Mesopotamia, to the banks of the Tigris and Euphrates. But exile did not stay its progress and it was enriched at that time by the prophecies of Ezechiel and Daniel. With the return from the great trial (538 B.C.) the Bible continued to grow.[5] Sometime in the second century before our era, one of the most noble books of the Old Testament, the Book of Wisdom (which we might consider as a prelude to the New Testament) was written at Alexandria, the intellectual capital of the world. Finally, with the four Gospels, the Acts of the Apostles, the twenty-one Epistles and the Apocalypse, the Bible attained its full stature. Though it will grow no more, it will never grow old, or fail.

Such, in broad outline, is the extraordinary biography of the *Unknown*. Let us now draw a few conclusions from this quick historical survey.

* * * * *

So ancient a book could not pass through so many centuries without paying some price for it. It was copied and translated time and time again. But des-

15

pite many accidents, lacunae, corruptions and trans-
positions, the Bible has kept its essential lines and is
still a good likeness of its original self; the wrinkles
of age have not altered its true appearance. Our present texts reproduce the original documents at least in
substance. In order to establish this substantial identity, scholars have collected and compared the testimony furnished over the course of centuries by manu-
scripts, versions and quotations. In the first three
chapters of Genesis, for example, there are about thirty
variant readings, but of such slight importance that
we can ignore them.

Secondly, as the Bible developed in such diverse
localities as the desert of Sinai, Palestine, or the shores
of the Tigris and Euphrates, it is not at all surprising
that the numerous and subtle influences of these regions played upon it. The land formed the Bible, as
it fashions men. In the Bible the most varied kinds of
countries are reflected; it takes to itself, as a living
organism takes external things to itself, images and
comparisons borrowed from all of these regions. In
the first chapter of Genesis we will come upon words,
images, scientific concepts and a folklore that belong
to the Assyro-Babylonian culture.[6] The Bible makes
us think of those ancients who have stored up in
memory the many souvenirs of a long life.

Finally, this book bears the imprint of a rich heritage. Its ancestry extends over fifteen centuries. Many
authors, both known and unknown, have worked to

produce it, and each of them has left stamped upon it something of his own personality. The extraordinary physiognomy of the Bible is due to the harmonious blending of the characteristics of its many forebears.

The Bible wears a halo of majesty, for it counts among its ancestors at least two monarchs: David, the beloved singer of Israel, and author of the principal part of the psalms, and Solomon, the great King whose wisdom surpassed that of the East and of Egypt. In the Bible we sometimes detect an aristocratic voice— Isaias, the most brilliant of the prophets, belonged to the ruling classes—and sometimes the realism, coarseness and fire of the lower classes—Amos, for example, was a sheep-raiser and a cultivator of fig trees—and sometimes the delicacy and religious sensitiveness of priestly souls like Jeremias, who was of a sacerdotal family, in whose voice there is a unique blending of religious and human tonality.[7]

What variety, then, and what contrasts! These authors are not copies of one another, even though they often exploit a common source. The first chapters of Genesis, for example, give two accounts of the creation of man, but the author of the first account may not even have known the second, so different are they.

"The style is the man." There are in the Bible, then, as many men—and there are many—as there are styles. In one book we encounter stiff, grammatically correct language, while another contains mistakes in words and syntax, and even crude expressions. Each author writes in a language which corresponds to his nationality, temperament and times. It is like a man in whose speech one can pick out all the dialectal differences of the land.

The Bible runs the whole gamut of human emotions, and to express them the Bible is fortunately able to draw upon a great variety of "literary forms." The sublimely eloquent discourses of Isaias, for example, surpass in splendor the orations of Athens and Rome. In the Psalms, the Bible throbs, sings, prays. (We often recite these religious poems without perceiving that they were originally poetry.) No poetical form is neglected, and it may well be that the Book of Job and the Canticle of Canticles are attempts at a dramatic form.

But the Bible shows a marked preference for history, not history in the modern manner, but a special history whose rules are still only partially known to us, although much better now than formerly. In the Bible we come across "certain fixed ways of expounding and narrating, certain definite idioms, especially of a kind peculiar to the Semitic tongue, so-called approximations and certain hyperbolical modes of expressions, nay, at times, even paradoxical, which help to impress the ideas more deeply on the mind."[8] These literary forms do not correspond to any of our classical categories, nor can they be judged in comparison with Graeco-Latin or modern literary forms. It is also a history unique in its kind, for it unfolds the epic story of humanity from the beginning of the world and of man up to the very end of time. From Genesis to the Apocalypse, the Bible opens for us the archives of the human race.

* * * * *

Before continuing our investigation further let us summarize the external characteristics of the *Unknown*. We know its name: *The Book;* its language, or better, its *languages;* its principal *lands* of origin, Arabia, Palestine, Assyro-Babylonia, Persia, Egypt; its *ancestry*, that is, its authors; the chief features of its *countenance* (its literary forms): eloquence, poetry, history.

All this is but the covering, the outward appearance. Now we must look more closely at what is below the surface. Let us terminate this first contact by delving deeper into the inner parts of the Book.

II

Men ordinarily reveal their character and personality by their interests and by the subjects they like to talk about. The Bible makes no attempt to hide its preferences and frequently returns to its favorite subjects.[9] Here we shall consider two particularly characteristic and especially striking themes, its faith in the one God, and its expectation of a mysterious being called *the Messiah*.

From the first page to the last, this complex book, born and raised in so many different regions, proclaims its **faith in one unique God** who is the Creator of the Universe, judge of all men, defender and avenger of morality. The Bible begins with the simple words: *In the beginning God created heaven and earth.* This initial declaration which seems so very natural and almost self-evident to us, raises the Bible above all the literatures of antiquity. Today after much historical research, we know of no other people of the Orient with so explicit a formula of faith as this.

The peoples surrounding the Jews all had pantheons wherein gods and goddesses were produced in prodigious abundance. At times these peoples felt the need of organizing their deities into a hierarchy at whose summit were a god-ruler and his goddess-queen. Thus, the Moabites worshipped Chamos and his goddess companion, Astarte; the Syrians venerated the divine couple Baal and Astarte. In Babylon, Marduk presided over the assembly of the gods, and in the Assyrian pantheon, Ashur held the primacy.

The Hebrews alone clung jealously to the concept of one God. They did indeed attribute various qualities to him, and gave him many names. In the first chapter of Genesis the Creator is called simply *Elohim*, that is, God, whereas in the two following chapters he has the two names *Yahweh-Elohim*. Then in the following pages, the Patriarchs invoke the *Eternal God*, the *God who sees*, the *God who acts*, the *God of Bethel*, the *Terror of Isaac*, the *Rock of Israel.* But "there is no more evidence of polytheism in this than in the Catholic custom of designating the Virgin Mary by the names of her shrines, her apparitions or her qualities; nobody has ever supposed that the Lady of Chartres, the Virgin of La Salette, and the Queen of Heaven are three different entities."[10] In all the stages of their history, despite the temptations which were ever before their eyes, despite the social pressure exerted upon them by the surrounding pagan populations, the people of the Bible preserved inviolate their faith in *Him who is.* This historical, but humanly inexplicable fact is enough to put the Book of this people in a class by itself.

*   *   *   *   *

Nor is this all. Biblical history, which is concerned with a period of almost two thousand years and which is made up of apparently disconnected fragments, is in reality an orderly history. In it we can see a tendency, a direction. Some secret inspiration animates it from within, unites and organizes the events, transforms the chaos of facts into a connected sequence.

In the third chapter of Genesis a mysterious, shadowy person, both human and superhuman, is introduced. At one and the same time he is the son of the woman and adversary of the devil. As a member of the human race he will wage victorious war against

21

the mortal enemy of our race and will thereby effect our spiritual liberation. Little by little his features emerge from the shadows and become clear. The Liberator will be born from among the Semites. Radiant as a star, he will rise from the line of Jacob. Son of a Virgin, monarch of all men, he will at the cost of his life inaugurate a beneficent rule whose splendor will dazzle the nations. In describing this monarch and his kingdom, the writers of the Bible exhaust their poetic vocabulary.[11] The Messiah fills the pages of the Old Testament with his invisible presence. "The Son of God is found sown throughout the Scriptures," said Saint Irenaeus. And the Doctor of Hippo, considering the Pentateuch, declared: "Moses speaks of Christ in everything that he wrote."[12] Deeds and men, the liturgy with its detailed rites, everything in the Book is oriented to the Messiah, as in a magnetic field iron filings take position around the magnet. It is Jesus Christ toward whom both testaments look—the Old in expectation, the New as to its model, both as their center. The first pages of the Bible resemble a dawn that is about to break; gradually the light grows stronger and finally brings day to the world. In the first pages of Genesis we contemplate these rays of the coming dawn.

*   *   *   *   *

The favorite subjects of the Bible have deeply intrigued the historians of religion. Scholars have sifted the sacred annals of Persia, carefully examined one of the oldest of human codes, that of Hammurabi, have dug deep into the royal chronicles of Sargon, Ashurbanipal, Nabuchodonosor, and into the poetical writings of India, Greece, Rome. But nowhere in the archives of other peoples have they discovered a phenomenon comparable to the one found in the Bible.

And yet the great civilized nations which were contemporary with the Bible could boast of undeniable advantages over Israel in the arts, sciences, philosophy, in political or military power. In India or Iran, for example, there were the empires of the Medes, the Persians, the Parthians, one succeeding the other; and the states in the Tigris and Euphrates basin had a well-developed literature and science. The Graeco-Roman world, and especially Greece, was famous for its philosophers, disciples of Plato and Aristotle.

But these peoples, so well-endowed, from a human point of view, bequeathed to prosperity writings filled with the grossest errors in the field of morality and religion. Israel, a people without art, without philosophy, without any great natural faculties, produced that incomparable wonder which is the Bible.

Should this observation lead us to conclude that a supernatural help was needed for the production of the Bible? This is not at all unreasonable, for where nature was most liberal among the cultured peoples of the East and the West, all efforts resulted in a complete failure; but among the Jews, where all means

23

for success were wanting, the attempt was crowned with success. This historical fact raises a problem impossible to evade. Every honest man owes it to himself to study the biblical writings with care, to weigh well what they have to say about themselves, and what has been determined regarding them by the religious society which has been nourished by these writings and has transmitted them to us.

Let us now see what the Bible says about itself, and also what the Church teaches about it. In this way we shall be able to understand something about *the Unknown.*

III

The first book of Machabees calls the group of Old Testament writings the *holy books* (12:9). Saint Paul referred to them as the *sacred letters* (II Tim 3:15-16). Why is the Bible *sacred* and *holy*?

Could it be because it contains a holy and sacred teaching or doctrine? The Bible does assuredly recount a sacred history, the history of the People of God. In addition, it teaches a holy doctrine, faith in one God and a morality which, in spite of its very real imperfections, outlines the perfect rule of the gospel. It tells the life-stories of men and women who are models of faith, holiness and self-sacrifice; the history of Joseph is a case in point. It gives us various prayers.

The Bible does, therefore, treat of a holy and sacred matter.

But is this sufficient reason for calling it the *holy book* or *sacred scripture?* Certainly not for Saint Paul, or for the Jewish and Christian traditions. The Baltimore catechism also contains a divine doctrine, a summary of sacred history, and prayers, but no one has ever considered it holy and sacred in the same way as the Bible.

Could it be because the Bible sanctifies those who read and meditate upon it with faith? No doubt the Bible, at least most of it, does exercise a sanctifying influence. "What things soever were written were written for our learning," writes Saint Paul, "that through patience and the comfort of the scriptures, we might have hope" (Rom 15:4). "The divine scriptures are the short roads to salvation. . . . The texts sanctify and divinize."[13] Hear Saint Thérèse of Lisieux, an expert in this matter: "It is from the gospels that I derive most help in the time of prayer. I find in their pages all that my poor soul needs, and I am always discovering there new lights, and hidden and mysterious meanings."[14]

Many other books, like the *Imitation of Christ,* the *Spiritual Combat* or the *Introduction to a Devout Life,* also arouse us from our spiritual torpor and draw us towards holiness. But the Bible, to which Christian tradition has always assigned a place by itself, derives its singular privilege from a cause not less singular: its divine origin gives the Bible its saintly and sacred character.

Saint Paul gives testimony that "all scripture is divinely inspired" (II Tim 3:16), that is, *breathed by God*. And Saint Peter clarifies this breath of God: "Holy men of God spoke, moved by the Holy Spirit" (II Peter 1:21). Moreover the Church, the infallible depositary of the apostolic teaching, has clearly explained for us what the Scriptures say about themselves, when she defined at the Vatican Council that the books of the Old and New Testament are sacred "because, written under the inspiration of the Holy Ghost, they have God for their author."[15]

As we have already seen, many authors, some known but most of them unknown, had a hand in the production of the Bible. Authors in the fullest sense of the term, these men lived at different times and reflect diverse periods and environments. Moreover, they were possessed of unequal intellectual resources. According to their individual temperament and purpose, they chose to use different literary forms. But one fundamental characteristic draws them together into a profound, mysterious, superhuman unity. All of them worked under the special influence of the Holy Ghost who made them his instruments. All of them vibrated under his influence, as strings of a harp under the touch of a musician. God illumined, but he did not destroy the way their minds worked; he guided their wills without destroying their freedom, helped them, but respected the delicate workings of human psychology. The Spirit of God moved them from within, as living instruments endowed with reason. We are not to compare them to speaking-tubes which join the divine world to ours, nor to loud-speakers which transmit the voice of God to us. God illumined, guided and assisted the sacred writers in such wise that these men expressed thoughts which were at the same time human and divine; the message which they formulated was both a human message and a message from God himself, the **Word of God**.[16]

Now we see why Jesus, the Apostle and the Church, in appealing to the Book, attributed undisputed authority to it. "It is written"; "the Scriptures testify"; "the Holy Spirit says," etc. and immediately all dispute ends, one bows before it. The Bible, the Word of God, imposes itself upon all minds. The Bible not only does not state nor imply error, it *cannot* state or imply it.[17] It is **infallible**.

We can also see why the Book conceals inexhaustible riches. The meaning of human words is quickly exhausted, but centuries of exploration have not succeeded in appraising all the treasures contained in the Bible. Origen, Saints Ephraim, Basil, Gregory of Nyssa, John Chrysostom, Jerome, Augustine, Bede, and many others have pored over the first pages of the Book in the hope of extracting from them the basic message they contain. Much remains still to be discovered. Every age emphasizes one or another aspect of the sacred account; each people, following its own bent, looks at the Bible from its own point of view. The Chinese and Japanese discern what has escaped the western mind; one century sees what another has been unaware of or had only dimly seen. Pius XII writes, "Moreover we may rightly and deservedly hope that our times also can contribute something towards the deeper and more accurate interpretation of Sacred Scripture. For not a few things, especially in matters pertaining to history, were scarcely at all or not fully explained by the commentators of past ages, since they lacked almost all the information which was needed for their clearer exposition. How difficult for the Fathers themselves, and indeed well nigh unintelligible, were certain passages, is shown, among other things, by the oft-repeated efforts of many of them to explain the first chapters of Genesis."[18]

Throughout the centuries and in every country, the sons of the Church, under the infallible direction of their Mother, by work and prayer draw from that Letter which has come to them from their heavenly home. "We walk in exile amid sighs and tears. And suddenly letters come to us from home." For when the human race was precipitated into the abyss of all vices, the Creator did not break off all relations with it; men had become unworthy of his friendship, but God wished to renew his friendship with them, and sent them letters, just as we do to those who are far away. The bearer of these Letters was Moses, and the first line of the message is: "In the beginning God created heaven and earth."[19]

In this way is explained the profound unity, the mysterious "directionism" which we have just admired. In every stage of its growth, the Book maintains its homogeneity despite the disparate materials which went into its make-up, because one and the same principal author watched over its formation. God was always on the project, whereas his many human collaborators succeeded one another. That is why biblical doctrine, morality and history progress after the fashion of a seed. It is a directed doctrine, a directed morality and a directed history. God is the responsible author who himself conceived and wrote this homogeneous doctrine and morality, this "magnetized" history, through the instrumentality of men whose will, mind and hands he guided.

Finally, we can understand why Christians from the greatest antiquity loved to carry a text of the Scriptures around with them and asked that passages from it be recited over their children. In times of persecution many chose to die rather than to give God's letters over to the enemies of the Church. Protestants and Jews manifest a like respect for the Bible. I have seen Jews devoutly rescue from Nazi flames the few pieces of the Bible roll spared by the fire.

Every Solemn High Mass speaks of the Church's veneration for the Holy Books. A special minister, the deacon, is deputed to read the Gospel. Before he does

so, the minister kneels to ask God to cleanse his heart
and his lips; to read and to understand the Book, his
soul must first be in harmony with its Author. Lacking sympathy, can anyone enter into the thought of a
writer? Here it is a question of being in tune with the
Holy Ghost, and the deacon feels the need of sanctifying and spiritualizing himself. Then, purified by his
prayer, the minister receives from the priest the special
blessing, an earnest of divine help. After this, the Book
is solemnly carried in procession. As a sign of respect,
those present in the Church rise to their feet. The
deacon incenses the text as one incenses the Body of
Christ at Benediction of the Most Blessed Sacrament.
Is not the Scripture the "verbal body" of the Word of
God? When the reading is finished the priest kisses
the inspired text.

These ceremonies are truly lessons in action, and
illustrate the truth which from now on will direct our
study: the Bible is the **Word of God**.

NOTES

1 *Oeuvres Pastorales* (1926), VI, 404.

    Fortunately, this situation has somewhat changed. As Cardinal Suhard notes, (*The Church Today* [Fides: Chicago, 1953], 204): "As a reaction against the Protestant doctrine based upon private interpretation, Catholics were long cut off from the infinite riches contained in the Word of God. Today that danger has disappeared and we are glad to recognize the movement, which daily grows stronger, in favor of the inspired books. . . . We encourage this movement, with the precautions necessary if one is to hold to the truths of the faith committed to the Church."

2 Genesis, Exodus, Leviticus, Numbers, Deuteronomy; Josue, Judges, Ruth, 1 and 2 Samuel, 1 and 2 Kings, 1 and 2 Chronicles, Esdras, Nehemias, Esther, 1 Machabees; Job, Psalms, Proverbs, Ecclesiastes, Canticles, Ecclesiasticus; Isaias, Jeremias, Lamentations, Baruch, Ezechiel, Daniel, Osee, Joel, Amos, Abdias, Jonas, Micheas, Nahum, Habacuc, Sophonias, Aggeus, Zacharias, Malachias.

3 Tobias, Judith (?), and the original text of the Gospel according to Saint Matthew. Aramaic fragments are found in Esd 4:8-6:18, 7:12-16; Dan 2:4-7; Jer 10:11; Gen 31:47.

4 The Biblical Commission in its response of June, 1906 instructed Catholic exegetes to maintain the Mosaic authenticity of the Pentateuch and its substantial in-

BEGINNINGS: GENESIS AND MODERN SCIENCE

tegrity. "The formula adopted by the Biblical Commission," notes Professor Coppens ("L'histoire critique de l'Ancien Testament," which appeared in the *Revue Théologique* [1938], 796), "is a particularly happy one and susceptible of a broad interpretation." The Secretary of the Biblical Commission in his recent letter (1948) substituted new and suggestive expressions for the terms of the old response: "We invite Catholic scholars to study the problems [of the composition of the Pentateuch] without prejudice, in the light of sound criticism and of the findings of other sciences which are connected with this subject. Such study will doubtless establish the great part and the deep influence exercised by Moses both as author and lawgiver" (*H P R,* 573). Father Bea, SJ, has noted the difference in the terminology of the two documents emanating from the Biblical Commission: "Formerly it was the custom to speak, in rather technical language, of the *substantial authenticity* and *Mosaic integrity* of the Pentateuch, whereas today we attribute to Moses *a great part* and *a profound influence* as *author* and *legislator.* Exegetes will be grateful for this definition of terms whose meaning has long been disputed. How can the 'substance' of the Pentateuch be explained? Do we mean substance in a material, quantitative sense, or in the ideal, including historical, ceremonial, legislative matters? And how shall we determine this substance?

"According to the Biblical Commission's recent letter, Moses is the author to whom the 'great part' of the Pentateuch is due. This clearly does not rule out his use of sources, nor those redactional processes referred to in the response of 1906. If the Biblical Commission does not frown upon the hypothesis of 'a progressive development of the Mosaic laws, due to social and religious conditions of later times, a development which is also manifest in the historical narratives,' it does not suggest that these accretions and additions are thereby simply subtracted from Moses' influence. All of the legislation contained in the Pentateuch is 'Mosaic,' that is, it derives either directly from Moses as its author and legislator, or, in the case of later additions, it is in the spirit of the ancient Mosaic legislation which it applies to new social and religious conditions. It is evident that the later additions which are not pure glosses must have been inspired, as the Biblical Commission had already stated in its response of June 27, 1906." Cf "Le Problème du Pentateuque et de l'Histoire primitive, En marge de la Lettre de la C B," *Civiltà Cattolica* (April, 1948), 120-121.

5   Among the post-exilic writings we may list Chronicles, Esdras, and Nehemias, Tobias, Esther, Judith, the two books of Machabees, some of the Psalms, Ecclesiastes, Canticles (?), Wisdom, Ecclesiasticus, Jonas (?), Aggeus, Zacharias, Malachias, very probably Joel, and perhaps the Trito-Isaias.

6   M J Lagrange, OP, "Hexaméron," *R B* 5 (1896), 405; "On Primitive History" (*Historical Criticism and the OT* [C T S, London, 1905], 180 ff); F Ceuppens, OP, *Historia Primaeva* (Rome, 1947), 51; R A F Mackenzie, SJ, "Before Abraham Was. . . ," *C B Q* 15 (1953), 131 ff; J L McKenzie, SJ, "The Literary Characteristics of Genesis 2-3," *Th* S 15 (1954), 541 ff.

7   Cf Daniel-Rops, *Sacred History*, 270.

8   *Divino Afflante Spiritu*, 37.

33

9   Cf A Gelin, *Les Idées Maitresses de l'Ancien Testa-ment* (Paris, Ed du Cerf, 1948).

10 Daniel-Rops, *Sacred History*, 60.

11 Gen 9:18-29; Num 24:14b-19; Gen 49:8-12; Is 7:14 ff; 53; 9:5; 9:29, etc.

12 Irenaeus, *Adv Haereses* 4:20; Augustine, *Contr Faust* 9:9; *P L* 42:320.

13 Clement of Alexandria, *Protreptikos* 9:8, 9; *P G* 8:188, 200.

14 *Saint Thérèse of Lisieux, Autobiography* (Kenedy & Sons, 1927), 147.

15 Enchiridion Symbolorum, 1787.

16 *Providentissimus Deus*, Nov 18, 1893 (Catholic Biblical Assoc, Wash, DC), 24: "The Holy Spirit . . . by his su-pernatural power so moved and impelled them to write —He so assisted them when writing—that the things which He ordered and those only, they first rightly understood, then willed faithfully to write down and finally expressed in apt words and with infallible truth."

17 *Ibid, loc cit*, "So far is it from being possible that any error can co-exist with inspiration, that inspiration not only is essentially incompatible with error, but ex-cludes and rejects it as absolutely and necessarily as it is impossible that God Himself, the supreme truth, can utter that which is not true."

18 *Divino Afflante Spiritu*, 31.

19 St. Augustine, *Enarratio in Psalmum* 149: *P L* 37:1952. Cf also St John Chrystostum, *Homilia in Gen 2:2; P G* 53:28.

CHAPTER TWO

"In the Beginning
God Created Heaven and Earth"

There is no problem more captivating than that of our origins. It is one that has arisen ever since "man began to be and to think." More than twenty centuries before the Christian era, at the time of the first Babylonian dynasty, scribes wrote on seven clay tablets the answer given by their ancestral traditions. Copies of this *Epic Poem of Creation,* one of the first examples of Akkadian literature, can be found in the Berlin and the London Museums.[1]

Despite many lacunae, these texts help us reconstruct a history of the formation of the world, a fantastic genesis sometimes grotesque and disconcerting to the western mind. Gods and goddesses rise two by two from the waters of the primitive chaos and proceed to engage in a merciless struggle among themselves. We witness the birth of monstrous beings: the hydra, the red dragon, scorpion-man, hurricane, fishman, capricorn. Finally, after titanic struggles between the divinized forces of nature, the world was formed.

Before the Babylonians, the Egyptian Paraohs of the 5th dynasty (from the 27th to the 26th century B.C.) covered the walls of their funerary chambers along the Nile with hieroglyphic writings. It was there that Maspero discovered what he called "the most ancient and the most complete body of doctrine which Egypt has left us." Those magnificent vertical inscriptions carved on the walls "evoke a time when heaven was not yet, nor was there any earth or man, the gods were not yet born, and death was not yet." From the primordial waters, on which there floated the seeds of all things, the sun-god, Ra, first emerged like the lotus flower or the papyrus, which in the early morning swims upon the waters and opens its petals. From Ra, the creator-god, came the gods and men, everything that lives upon the earth and in heaven.

Some few specialists—philologists, and historians, or those of a curious bent of mind—will always take an interest in these old Egyptian and Babylonian documents. But who takes these texts seriously? No one would dream for a moment of giving them any objective value. And no one ever considers going to such documents for relief from the anxieties that trouble the hearts of men.

The interest attaching to the first chapters of the Bible is something quite different. The traditions of Babylon are diluted in a flood of words, and those of Egypt are spread out over many square feet of wall, but the answer given in the Bible takes up less than fifty lines. This answer may stir the curiosity of men of science, who love ancient lore, but in some it leads to decisive reactions in the domain of conscience. It is brief, original, profound, unrivalled. Yes, unrivalled. Many have attempted—and wrongly—to contradict it with the answers of science. Carefully remove the misunderstandings and equivocations, define the different points of view, and delimit their respective fields, and there exists neither opposition nor conflict between faith and science. Both should be able to get along with one another. Far from being opposed, they complement one another.

I

From childhood on, the text of the Bible sings in our memory. But let us reread it so as to refresh that memory.

In the begining God (Elohim) created the heavens and the earth; the earth was waste and void; darkness covered the abyss, and the spirit of God was stirring above the waters. (1:1-2.)

37

God (Elohim) said "Let there be light," and there was light. God (Elohim) saw that the light was good. God (Elohim) separated the light from the darkness, calling the light Day and the darkness Night. And there was evening and morning, the first day. (1:3-5.)

Then God (Elohim) said, "Let there be a firmament in the midst of the waters, to divide the waters." And so it was. God (Elohim) made the firmament, dividing the waters that were below the firmament from those that were above it. God (Elohim) called the firmament Heaven. And there was evening and morning, the second day. (1:6-9.)

Then God (Elohim) said, "Let the waters below the heavens be gathered into one place and let the dry land appear." And so it was. God (Elohim) called the dry land Earth and the assembled waters Seas. And God (Elohim) saw that it was good. Then God (Elohim) said, "Let the earth bring forth vegetation: seed-bearing plants and all kinds of fruit trees that bear fruit containing their seed." And so it was. The earth brought forth vegetation, every kind of seed-bearing plant and all kinds of trees that bear fruit containing their seed. God (Elohim) saw that it was good. And there was evening and morning the third day. (1:9-13.)

And God (Elohim) said, "Let there be lights in the firmament of the heavens to separate day from night; let them serve as signs for the fixing of the seasons, days and years; let them serve as lights in the firmament of the heavens to shed light upon the earth." So it was. God (Elohim) made the two great lights, the greater light to rule the day, and the smaller one to rule the night, and he made the stars. God (Elohim) set them in the firmament of the heavens to shed light upon the earth, to rule the day and the night and to separate the light from the darkness. God (Elohim) saw that it was good. And there was evening and morning, the fourth day. (1:14-19.)

Then God (Elohim) said, "Let the waters abound with life, and above the earth let winged creatures fly below the firmament of the heavens." And so it was. God (Elohim) created the great sea monsters, all kinds of living, swimming creatures with which the waters abound and all kinds of winged birds. God (Elohim) saw that it was good and blessed them, saying, "Be fruitful, multiply and fill the waters of the seas; and let the birds multiply on the earth." And there was evening and morning, the fifth day. (1:20-23.)

God (Elohim) said, "Let the earth bring forth all kinds of living creatures; cattle, crawling crea-

*tures and wild animals." And so it was. God
(Elohim) made all kinds of wild beasts, every
kind of cattle, and every kind of creature crawling on the ground. And God (Elohim) saw that
it was good. (1:24-25.)*

*God (Elohim) said, "Let us make mankind in
our image and likeness; and let them have dominion over the fish of the sea, the birds of the
air, the cattle, over all the wild animals and every
creature that crawls on the earth." God (Elohim)
created man to his image. In the image of God
he created him. Male and female he created
them. Then God (Elohim) blessed them and said
to them, "Be fruitful and multiply; fill the earth
and subdue it. Have dominion over the fish of
the sea, the birds of the air, the cattle and all the
animals that crawl on the earth." God (Elohim)
also said, "See, I give you every seed-bearing
plant on the earth and every tree which has
seed-bearing fruit to be your food. To every
wild animal of the earth, to every bird of the
air, to every creature that crawls on the earth
and has the breath of life, I give the green plants
for food." And so it was. God (Elohim) saw that
all he had made was very good. And there was
evening and morning, the sixth day. (1:26-31.)*

*Thus the heavens and the earth were finished
and all their array [armies]. On the sixth day*

*God (Elohim) finished the work he had been do-
ing. And he rested on the seventh day from all
the work he had done. God (Elohim) blessed the
seventh day and made it holy because on it he
rested from all his work of creation. This is the
story of the heavens and the earth at their creation. (2:1-4a.)*

II

Does this account, which is much later than the
Babylonian and Egyptian narratives, go back in its
actual form to the time of Moses, that is, to the 13th
or 15th century B.C.? Probably not. Critics in ever-
increasing number question the Mosaic origin of our
redaction, and with reason. It is hazardous to venture
a *date* in this matter, but there is nothing to prevent
us from admitting the *Mosaic character of the traditions* which are condensed in this theological résumé.[2]
Before being mummified in writing and fixed in the
form so familiar to us, the tradition regarding the
origin of the world was engraved on men's memories,
and had to be transmitted orally. We who live in the
age of the newspaper, and who so readily depend upon the "memory of paper," can only with difficulty
understand and appreciate the role once played by
oral tradition. In former times the learned man was
not one who had read much, but one who had heard

much. Long before they were putting into writing, the poems of Homer, the sacred traditions of Persia, the maxims of the Jewish Talmud, and the sayings of the Koran were recited or declaimed. Even today some peoples without literature transmit their histories, without notable corruption, by word of mouth.

So it was with the Patriarchs, the ancestors of the Hebrew peoples; from father to son, from master to pupil, ancient traditions concerning the origin of the world and of man were communicated by word of mouth. The day came when an author inspired by God set down the account of the origins in the form which has become familiar to us.

This familiar, inspired account of the beginnings of man and the universe first gives us, in two short sentences, a **preamble** (1:1-2); then the **narrative** proper (1:3-31); finally a short **epilogue** (2:1-4a).

❋   ❋   ❋   ❋   ❋

The preamble succinctly sets forth the theme of the narrative: "In the beginning God (Elohim) created the heavens and the earth." And at the same time it gives us the key and the division of the account: "the earth was waste and void." In the account itself we shall see how the earth was "formed" and "filled." It will be "formed" because God will inject order where disorder reigned, in the *tohu-bohu,* as the Hebrew text puts it; this will be the work of the first three days, the first triduum (1:3-13). The earth will then be "filled," for God will arrange and ornament the empty space by creating the "army of the heaven and of earth"; this will be the work of the last three days, or the second triduum. After the work, there follows the rest which is mentioned in the epilogue (2:1-4a).

Nothing could be simpler, nothing easier to keep in mind than this symmetrical division.[3] It sticks in the mind because it is based on everyday life. The framework of the divine work closely copies the work of man: the Hebrews worked during the day, stopped working at night, resumed it in the morning; and this for six days in a row. On the seventh day they abstained from work. The divine Artisan is likewise portrayed as working during the day, stopping at night, taking up the work in the morning, and all this too for six days.

This setting had this great advantage, that it recalled in a concrete manner an important religious duty, the sanctification of the sabbath. It was full of meaning for a people so fond of symbolism.[4] It is, however, difficult to deny the liturgical intent of the author. If his text does not promulgate for the first time the law of the sabbath rest, it at least alludes to it. The impression is given that the sabbath was in full swing at the time the Mosaic cosmogony was set down in writing. An allusion suffices to recall what everyone knows. A hitherto unknown law, on the contrary, is not so promulgated. Following the example of God (Ex 20:11), the Hebrews, like free men (Deut 5:15), will rest on the sabbath day.

Within the narrative, as a memory-help or pedagogical device, the author multiplies key-words. The reader will easily notice the repetitious, stereotyped formulas which recur at regular intervals, like refrains, according to what seems to be an intentional order. These peculiarities give the narrative a rhythm and a cadence all its own. Couplets of the same structure begin and end using the same words and phrases: "And God said. . . ." "Let this or that be done. . . ." "And it was done. . . ." "And there was evening and morning." Many attempts have been made to discover the secret of this rhythm. We must take care not to attribute to the results of such analysis an importance which it perhaps does not possess, but still, literary analysis does bring out the artificial structure and schematism of the narrative. These slight but convergent indications[5] manifest the author's intention: perhaps with pedagogical purpose, he arranges, composes and invents a meaningful framework well within the grasp of his listeners or readers.

With reference to this narrative mention is often made of a "popular account." This is somewhat equivocal. The designation is correct if by it we mean that this narrative is well-adapted to the people, and to the intelligence and memory of the Hebrews. But this studied and successful adaptation bespeaks much knowledge and art. We willingly grant that we have here a popular account very skilfully put together, comparable to certain pages of catechetical explanation which bear the imprint of a theologian.

Let us immediately draw a most important conclusion. According to the findings of biology, geology and paleontology, the history of our universe embraces hundreds of millions of years. According to Lapparent, "Historians, of ancient as well as of modern history, count by centuries. For proto-history the unit of measure is no longer the century but the millenium. Pre-historians and the specialists in the Quaternary Period must certainly count in tens of thousands of years. Strata-minded geologists, finally, who study the Tertiary, the Secondary, the Primary and the Pre-Cambrian ages, must take a million years as their basis; that is the unit of geological time. . . . What is certain, as everyone knows, is this: the coal in our mines was formed hundreds of millions of years ago. Thus the length of the Pre-Cambrian period alone is greater than that of the three eras, Primary, Secondary, Tertiary, put together." And the same author gueses at some numbers: "According to estimates most worthy of credence . . . the whole Primary-Quaternary duration lasted 500,000 years, whereas the part of the Pre-Cambrian Period accessible to our study alone lasted 750,000 years."[6]

It would be childish to question the value of these scientific findings on the pretext that geologists do not agree as to the exact dates of things. Despite the uncertainty and undeniable arbitrariness of the numbers furnished, it remains true that our universe was being formed over a period of milions of years.

But it would be equally childish to become panicky, as if science gave the lie to the Bible.

In order to get a picture of the history of the universe, scientific men divide the history of our planet into four great geological eras. They then subdivide these eras into periods, and attempt to calculate the duration of the geological periods as accurately as they can. The choice of these methods and the technical structure of their writings give us some idea of their purpose, which is to describe in as accurate a way as possible the course of the world's history, its precise modalities, and its approximate duration.

The sacred author did not pose as a scientist, nor pursue a scientific purpose. This does not mean that he possessed no scientific learning, even of the most rudimentary kind. But he was not interested in knowing the duration of the world's evolution. His interest was in a reality of the utmost importance in the religious life of his people, namely, God, the Author of everything that exists. He made an effort to bring this reality close to the understanding of his contemporaries by means of the setting which his art had suggested to him.

We should, then, not set science against faith, nor the conclusions of modern scientists against our ancient author. Were we to do so, we would be posing a false problem. Let the scientists continue, in complete independence, to measure the rate of erosion by rivers, to calculate the age of sedimentary deposits according to their radioactive properties.[7] The results of their work will never contradict the "six days" of the Bible, for the Bible moves on an entirely different plane.

* * * * *

In the previous section we have taken the framework apart and have examined the mold. Let us now see what material the artist put into this frame and poured into the mold.

The Universe comes from God; this is the essential **content** of this narrative. You will look in vain for the term "universe" in the first chapter of Genesis. The word does not even exist in the language. The Greeks, those worshippers of reason and beauty, called the universe the *Cosmos,* that is, order, ornament; the Jews rendered it freely by, *the heavens and the earth.*

How did they look upon these heavens and this earth?

Surely not as we do. For a century now our telescopes and astronomical instruments have been probing into space and have discovered millions of galaxies. Each of these galaxies is made up of millions of stars. Beyond our solar universe, through astonishing distances of space, lie numberless other universes. For us the Universe is an enormous machine with many complicated sets of wheels.

47

But the Hebrew had only his two eyes with which to catalogue the heavens and the earth. Moreover, as an observer he was less careful, less clever than his neighbors from the region of the Tigris and Euphrates, who delved deeply into the mysteries of the starry heavens; picturing the world in a very elementary way, he simply divided the universe into several zones.

There was, first of all, his own domain, the solid earth; as far as he was concerned it was the most important region. Then, up over his head he placed a sphere limited and sustained by a vast, apparently solid expanse, like a roof. As a matter of fact, the heavenly vault does look like a roof for the world, and our romantic writers sometimes speak of the dome of the heavens. Between the "extent of the heavens" and the "face of the earth" is an immense space comparable to the abyss of the waters, where "every winged thing that flies" moves about. Our author had some difficulty naming this space, for his language has no suitable term for it. He extricates himself from his difficulty by the use of an awkward circumlocution; it is the "region above the earth." Finally, to complete the enumeration of the zones of the universe he mentions the "abyss of the waters." The world seemed, to the ordinary eye, to be thus divided.

These regions are inhabited. Numerous forms of beings move about in the heavens, in the abyss of the air, in the abyss of the waters, on the face of the earth; they form the "army of the heavens and the earth."

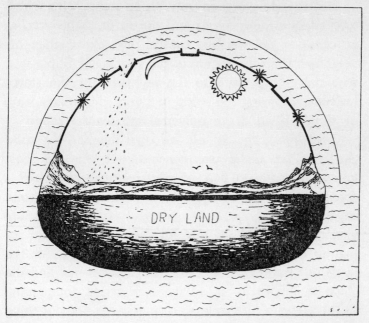

DRY LAND

HEBRAIC CONCEPTION OF THE WORLD

Why the name "army"? Perhaps because of the order and discipline which prevailed in this world; or perhaps it was the way living things swarm and group together that suggested the military metaphor.

There will be no complete "review" of the army of the heavens and the earth here. The sacred author, with his penchant for classification, gives a simplified list of the various categories of beings. He is not pursuing a scientific goal, even though he thus reveals something of his worldly culture to us.

49

The army of the heavens comprised a great light "to rule the day," a smaller light, the moon, "to rule the night," and the stars. From the point of view of usefulness the sun and moon are of special interest, for they regulate the succession of days, they fix the dates of the calendar, and they indicate the seasons of the year. Next is the army of the twofold abyss of the water and air. The "army of the air" takes in all winged things, birds and insects. It is hard to describe the "army of the seas," but it was made up of the great sea monsters and the fishes of smaller size. Finally, the army of the earth is grouped under three headings: cattle, reptiles and the wild beasts under the dominion of man.

A short, superficial, incomplete listing of names, all this, yet such an all-embracing, systematic, pseudoscientific enumeration was amply sufficient for the purpose in hand. By dividing the world loosely into four regions the sacred author took in the whole universe; similarly, by means of this schematic and "scholarly" grouping he designated all beings.[8]

According to the biologists, you may object, there are 600,000 distinct species of animal life, more than 800,000 of plant life, and new ones are being discovered every day.

All this may very well be so, we answer. Let the biologists go on with their researches and their inventory of the riches of the world. The Bible does not hold back the investigations of science. Its purpose, of another order, is to teach the people a *religious* truth, namely, everything that moves about in the water, the air, the earth is the work of God.

*   *   *   *   *

How in the fictitious framework of a week, is the inspired author going to describe the work of the Creator? What **order** will he follow?

Before setting to work a workman gathers his materials together. From the first lines of the narrative God is in possession of the material which he will use for the construction of the world. He will make use of it as one who has complete mastery over it. And while in pagan literature Ra or Marduk, the pagan god-creator, emerges from the primordial chaos, here Elohim is in no wise dependent upon matter; on the contrary, matter depends utterly upon him.

The materials of the world are heaped together in a state of confuison; there was a *tohu-bohu,* the author says, making use of an old popular term which brings to mind the mythology of the Babylonian traditions. The earth and waters intermingle; deep darkness envelops this shapeless mass. Above the chaos hovers the vivifying breath of God, probably the atmospheric air.[9] The hagiographer is not narrating the origin of disorder, but he mentions this chaos to express the notion of order. Left to themselves the earth and heaven would be nothing but disorder; the first word of God, therefore, was to unravel this confusion, to separate these chaotic elements.

But a man has to see what he is doing, for one cannot work in the dark. This is one of the reasons God created light in the very beginning: "Let there be light." He established the succession of light and darkness and instituted the day. "And there was evening and morning, the first day." With this time began to run its course, days were to succeed days, weeks weeks, months months. We are truly *in the beginning*. And it was God who imparted the initial movement. By placing the creation of light at the very beginning of everything, the inspired author not only showed his respect for common ordinary sense—no one works in darkness—but he also asserted in this concrete manner God's absolute mastery over time.

But although the sacred writer was understood by his immediate listeners and hearers, he has not escaped the criticism of later readers. How explain the regular succession of light and darkness without the sun? How explain the stars, which made their appearance only two days later? A classic difficulty. In order to tone down or suppress such scientific heresy, exegetes have exhibited much ingenuity. Some have identified the light of the first day with the "diffused light emanating from the original nebula," others with the "energy, at first obscure, by whose action the primitive chaos was first to clear up, and then later to become luminous." Many thought that the stars were "created" in the beginning, but did not "appear" until the fourth day. They paraphrase the divine command somewhat in this manner:

"Let there be light on the face of the earth, that is, because of a purified terrestrial atmosphere, let the light of the sun be able to penetrate the surface of our planet and favor the growth of plant life. And it was so. And in that airy setting purified of dark vapors, there suddenly appeared the disks of the Sun and of the Moon, which became signs to measure time."[10]

This is really not a true problem. The Hebrews had often noticed that despite the absence of the sun (as for example on dark and gloomy days) there was light. And as every morning light preceded the rising of the sun, they concluded that light was in some way independent of the sun. What precisely was their scientific idea? Who can say? When at the beginning of the second three-days, the sun was commanded "to rule the day," its role was perhaps thought to consist in emphasizing by its presence the separation of the day from the night, and to act as a sign for the establishing of the calendar. The sun was to illuminate the earth; it was not, however, to be the sole and exclusive source of light.

Thus "day" was made by the separation and alternate appearance of light and darkness. It was the first "putting in order."

After the interruption of the night, the divine worker continued his "work of distinction" by separating the lower from the upper waters. As rain falls from the upper regions of the firmament, there had to be reservoirs of water there. Hence the need of a solid support to hold back the watery masses. The "firmament," conceived of as a vault, served this purpose. This inverted bowl, in which there were windows, flood-gates and trap-doors through which the rain could pour as through a lattice, was thought to rest upon the extremities of the earth, on the horizon, where heaven and earth met. Therefore, the creation of the firmament meant the formation of the two regions of the universe, the abyss of the waters and the abyss of the air. This was the second bit of "putting in order."

One day remains of the first triduum. On this day the principal zones of the world were constituted. At the command of God dry land emerged and was separated from the lower waters, the seas. With the dry land came the plants. Material and inert as the ground itself, vegetation did not form part of the "army" whose creation is described in the second part of the narrative. God will now proceed to fit out the major regions of the world.

The first day of the second triduum (the fourth day), Elohim injected order into the luminous and dark part of the natural day. In the heavens he placed the sun, the moon and the stars. On the second day (the fifth creative day), he peopled the abyss of the waters with an "abundance of living things," and the abyss of the air with "every winged thing that flies."

Finally on the third day (the sixth of creation), after he had produced the land animals, God created his masterpiece, man.

Does the **order** of the appearance of the regions of the universe and their armies correspond to *reality*? In other words, was it the intention of the narrator in the Bible to imply that the history of the world actually unfolded as follows: first the separation of light from darkness, then the separation of the upper waters from the lower, and finally the emergence of dry land? Does the Bible claim to teach us that the order of the formation of beings was: first the stars, then the birds and fishes, finally land animals and man?

Without any hesitation we answer these questions in the negative. Let us not demand of the Bible what we have a right to look for only in a study on biology or botany or zoology or anthropology. It would be useless to look for a chronology, loose or exact, in an exposition or field wherein an artificial pattern has the last word, and, more to the point, where the pattern is influenced by scientific opinions far removed from those of our own times.

The author whom God used for the transmission of his message had the secular culture of his own times. In particular, he shared the pseudo-scientific notions of his contemporaries, rudimentary notions based on empirical knowledge and daily observation. He most certainly expressed himself in accordance with the concrete facts of his own experience; he described natural

55

phenomena externally, or as they appeared to be. For him, as for us, the sun seemed larger than the moon, and seemed to move in the firmament from east to west. But how can we hold this against him when we ourselves speak of the rising and the setting of the sun?

Let us go further. The sacred author not only allowed himself to be guided by the facts of experience in the language that he used—and in so doing he neither errs nor leads us into error—but he also communicated the divine thought to us through the medium of the scientific notions of his times. These notions were part of the mental structure imposed on him by his own civilization. His conception of the world and his vision of the universe, the mere sketch of a truly scientific system, shaded and colored his language. He would have expressed himself differently if he had known of the real dimensions of the universe, of the condensation of vapor, and the theories of the tides. But when God made use of the sacred author in speaking to men, he did not substitute a more scientific *mentality* for the elementary secular culture of his instrument; he did not wipe out the intellectual habits of his messenger to replace them with a new mental structure. Had he done this—a hypothesis contrary to psychology and thus practically impossible—the account of creation would perhaps have been given to us in the following manner:

"In the beginning, that is, about two billion years ago, the earth, a tiny bit of an immense gaseous mass, was projected into space more than 100,000 miles from the sun, of which it is nothing but an unimportant fragment, not even one-millioneth as large in size. God caused life to appear gradually on this earth; the operation took more than 800,000 years to produce the various kinds of plants and animals, culminating finally in the creation of man."

We can easily imagine the effect such a statement would have had upon his readers: bewilderment, stupefaction, incredulity, indignation. Could the sun be so large, the earth so little? Was the Almighty so weak that he needed millions of years to complete his work?

But God did not upset the mental workings of his instrument. He respected his faulty science and the way his mind worked. Why not? It was not God's intention to teach men "how heavens go, but how to go to heaven." Under the inspiration of the Holy Spirit the sacred author simply expressed himself in accordance with his own primitive theories. He was not writing in order to propose, assert or imply his "scientific notions"; the interests of a science teacher were not his interests. But his deep-seated hidden opinions, things taken for granted, so colored his language that we can divine or guess what his personal convictions were.

Consider an example. During the months that precede a presidential election, the speeches and conventions and platforms occasion much comment. There is much partisan argument, many wild statements made by indiscreet propagandists; but there is also peaceful "conversation" on the part of men whose one concern is to be objective. Is it not a fact that in all these instances it is possible to tell, by the manner in which the speakers express themselves, their internal choice, their secret tendencies, their social or political mentality? These men may not intend to state their preference, nor the side to which they are inclined, and in some cases, at least, they positively exclude this intention, for one reason or another. Yet a political mentality, a concept of economy or society, shines through the criticisms or judgments which they bring to bear on persons or events. Why? Because a man's pronouncements reveal, willingly or not, his inner state of mind. Between what he *deliberately intends* to say, therefore, and what he may privately think about a certain subject there may be a vast difference—a significant difference for our interpretation of Sacred Scripture, for the inspired author's private opinions are not guaranteed by God but only his deliberate, intended, "official" pronouncements..

Thus, on reading the first chapter of Genesis we can perceive the scientific notions of the author; they are, by the way, erroneous. He shares them with his contemporaries, but properly speaking he does not express them, does not affirm them, nor is it his intention to imply them.[11]

He speaks in conformity with his personal views; moreover, he organizes his narrative according to his own pseudo-scientific logic. He could put the creation

of the light on the first day and before the production
of the stars, because in his mind light was independent
of the sun; he could describe the formation of the
firmament in relation to the separation of the waters,
because he thought there were reservoirs of water in
the upper region of the world.

We think, then, that the **order** in which the regions
of the universe and the inhabitants appeared was, in
the thought of the author, *purely logical* (that is, artificial), not chronological (that is, real and natural)—a
deliberate and artistic disposition of his materials which
in no way affects the underlying historical reality affirmed by the sacred writer, the fact of creation by
God.[11a] It was the logic of a good workman who proceeds in an orderly and methodical manner, a logic
influence by the "science" of his times; it was above
all the logic of a religious soul whose one care was to
point out that all nature is directed toward man, the
image of God. Before introducing the king, God prepared the castle and created the servants of the monarch. We do not deny, however, that there may actually be at least a rough sort of agreement between this
logical order and the real order recorded by science.
We can admit this harmony, if there be one, but we
are not proposing any form of concordism.*

How did the universe reach its present form? It
is the business of scientists to discuss this freely. Let

---

*For concordism, see *supra,* p. 3.

them scrutinize the geological strata, flourish their tele-scopes, and go into spectroscopy and astrophysics. Should we follow Laplace in explaining the origin of the planets and their satellites by the condensation of the stellar substance, or, as many moderns hold, by the coming together of the stars? Did another sun once pass close to our sun and tear from it part of its substance, which then became Mercury, Venus, Mars, Jupiter, Saturn, Uranus, Neptune, Pluto and our Earth? Was there originally a kind of primeval radioactive atom, a single bit of matter in a state of condensation, which later broke down into a giant fireworks display which generated our universe? The Bible allows all these cosmogonic hypotheses; it does not contradict them; it preserves a strict neutrality. It would enter a protest only if the scientist, stepping out of his own proper field and making an abusive use of his own specific methods, were to attempt to eliminate the in-tervention of the Creator.

Our text, with its naive scientific notions, contains a teaching unknown to the ancient literatures. Heaven and earth, that is, the world in its entirety, depend upon a single God, and this unique God is dependent upon nothing. According to Assyro-Babylonian and Egyptian documents, the divinity which organized the universe rose from the primitive chaos; in the Bible we are shown the Lord as the absolute master of a matter which he fashions as he pleases. Creation is conceived neither after the manner of a struggle between the gods, nor after the manner of a divine generation—these are the two principal mythological modes—but as a divine work having results in time. In order to describe this work the sacred author twice used a word which the biblical vocabulary reserves to God, *bara,* or *create.* It is to be noted that the word is used twice: once to announce the origin of all things, (Gen 1:1), and then to introduce the first living beings (Gen 1:21).

God, then, does not depend upon matter, but matter depends upon God. This relation we shall call *creation.* We would not dare assert that the author of the first chapter of Genesis formally teaches a creation out of nothing, but he puts his readers on the path to that doctrine. Little by little, thanks to the stimulation of the Holy Spirit, that idea grew, and the day came when the formal notion of creation was clearly expressed in the Bible (II Mach 7:28). It is true that the human mind can surely arrive at this truth by itself, but as a matter of fact the greatest minds of antiquity, outside of Judaism, barely had an inkling of it. The Jews owe their superiority on this point to revelation. Christian philosophers were later on to re-discover and demonstrate by their own reason this truth which the Bible "breathed" to them.[12]

God was present at the origin of matter. When life began, God was there. But when did this life spring forth on our globe? The Bible gives no clearcut answer here, since the framework of the six days does not correspond to reality. How did life begin? Was there a single living cell at the beginning of the vital current, or rather, as the majority of scientists would have it, did life arise on many parts of the globe at the same time under different forms? How were the material corpuscles vitalized? Did life spontaneously burst forth within the raw matter?

These are the many questions with which our contemporaries harass the Bible. And they are questions for which there are no answers, for how could the sacred author answer questions which he would not have dreamed of asking? With deliberate insistence he repeats his fundamental assertion that all living beings, all plant and animal species, derive their origin from God.

It is God who created the "great sea monsters and all kinds of living, swimming creatures with which the waters abound and all kinds of winged birds" (Gen 1:21). It is God who made "all kinds of wild beasts, every kind of cattle and every kind of creature crawling on the ground" (Gen 1:25). It is God, finally, who "created man in his image" (Gen 1:27).

But as to the mode of the divine intervention, it is not certain that the author of the first chapter of Genesis wished to be very precise. Life emanates from God. But how? The waters abound with "all kinds of living beings"; but how were the sea monsters and the fishes of the ocean made? Was it from pre-existing matter or not? The first chapter gives us no an-

62

swer. It is equally silent as to the origin of the birds, and it is silent as to the way God created man. Let us simply state that as far as the sacred writer was concerned, such questions did not have the same importance as they have for us.[13]

There appears to be more precision regarding the land animals. "God (Elohim) said, Let the earth bring forth all kinds of living creatures . . . and God (Elohim) made all kinds of wild beasts." The land animals were apparently drawn forth from the soil. The author may simply have intended to draw a contrast between purely material, earthly animals and man, who was created in the image of God. In any case, the sacred text should not be cited for or against spontaneous generation, for or against the evolution of species. The Bible stands on neutral ground.

There is much confusion on this point, and we should deal with it here. Imagine two students of a liberal university, one of them a Catholic, arguing about the existence of God. The unbeliever declares that God does not exist, as will soon be proved when science produces life in the laboratory; the young Catholic maintains that God does exist because no one will ever be able to produce life synthetically.

As if our belief in God the Creator were bound up with the existence or non-existence, past or future, of spontaneous generation! We need not fear the test tubes of the scientists. Scientists have achieved notable successes. They have produced organic bodies such as hormones, insulin, thyroxin, adrenalin, which in times past only living bodies could produce. In their laboratories they have constructed increasingly complex bodies which from a molecular and structural point of view resemble living albumin. They have tracked down the mysterious filterable virus found at the very fringe of living and non-living being. Will they one day be able to produce a synthetic life? Will they be able to prove that matter becomes living matter as the result of chemical reactions? We do not know, and it would be foolish for us to play the prophet. One thing is certain: the experiments of scientists cannot contradict the Bible, which has nothing to say about the way animal life originated or how life came to be. Christian theologians and philosophers need not be disturbed. The atom is endowed with chemical affinities whereby it can unite in many different ways with other atoms, and by its dynamic force assumes the marvelous forms known to mineralogists. Why then might it not, if the Creator so wished, be able to endow itself with organs in that stupendous thing we call the living cell?[14]

An allied question is that of the differentiation of plant and animal, fossil and existing species, the subject-matter of zoology and botany. The Bible sheds no light on the solution of this problem, inasmuch as the first chapter of Genesis is "a popular account in which the author clearly teaches that God is the author of life, and that all the fishes and birds in their kind

and the land animals too depend on God and owe their
origin and existence to him. . . ." As to the scientific
theories regarding the origin and evolution of species,
the author says nothing, he does not even think of
them. There is, therefore, nothing in favor of and nothing against the theory of the transformation of species.[15]

This statement of modern exegetes is not dictated
by a tacit opportunism calculated to avoid all conflict between science and faith. Neither Saint Gregory
of Nyssa nor Saint Augustine, who were understandably unacquainted with the theory of transformism,
looked upon the creation of beings in their present
stage as forming part of the deposit of faith. According to them, God in the beginning created the vegetable and animal species in a loosely defined state; he
produced the "principles, powers, causes, the *rationes
seminales*, the seeds of seeds," which at a given moment would, without the special intervention of God
but under the direction of his providence, blossom
forth into many species.[16] Christian philosophers aware
of the modern scientific currents have again taken up,
completed, developed and supported these ideas. The
Dominican, Père Sertillanges, a genuine disciple of
Saint Thomas, says: "Transformism as a general procedure of nature for the coming forth and distribution
of life on earth remains to be proved. . . . But science's
last word has not yet been spoken. If transformism
should one day win its case, Thomistic philosophy has
nothing to fear, for its doctrine is wide open to so at-

tractive an hypothesis, precisely because it is so all-embracing. In these times Thomism ought to adapt itself to modern chemistry, so different from ancient science which considered such statements as 'Fire begets fire' and 'Air begets air' as axiomatic. Chemical transformism is a fact; before our very eyes the scientist causes the appearance of new species. Who will say that this was impossible, that it has always been impossible in regard to life? Thomistic philosophy is wide open to the theory of transformism and awaiting the day when transformism will have become scientifically something more than an hypothesis."[17]

*　　*　　*　　*　　*

The first page of the Bible has nourished Christian and Jewish devotion and has furnished topics of meditation for religious souls.

"O Lord, our Lord,
　　How glorious is your name over all the earth. . . .
When I behold your heavens, the work of your fingers,
　　The moon and the stars which you set in place—
What is man that you should be mindful of him,
　　Or the son of man that you should care for him?
You have made him little less than the angels,
　　And crowned him with glory and honor.
You have given him rule over the works of your hands,
　　Putting all things under his feet:
All sheep and oxen,

Yes, and the beasts of the field,
The birds of the air, the fishes of the sea,
And whatever swims the paths of the seas.
O Lord, our Lord,
How glorious is your name over all the earth!" (Ps 8)

Religious admiration in view of the marvels that reflect the *Name* (that is, the perfections) of God, his wisdom, power, goodness; a realization of man's eminent dignity as lord of the world and viceroy of the universe; loving gratitude towards so bountiful a Master—these are the feelings that stirred the soul of the psalmist.

In our day there are not too many who feel this way, because they fail to understand the divine murmur, or hardly hear that mysterious language in which all things in the universe speak to us.[18] For many of us the universe has become an undecipherable book. True, we have discovered and harnessed invisible powers of nature. We live in an age of electricity, planes, radios, atom and hydrogen bombs and write mathematical equations for the laws that regulate the movement of the stars. But modern man, proud of his techniques and fascinated by his discoveries and inventions, has lost sight of God. And at the same time he no longer becomes enthusiastic over his contact with real things. . . . As if his electric lights had eclipsed the splendor of the sun! As if his knowledge of the laws of nature had lessened the majesty of the Creator!

67

Because modern man no longer understands the value, the complete significance of all the beings that surround him, or the religious meaning of creation, he no longer sings of the "beautiful, radiant sun," of the water "useful, lowly, precious, chaste," of fire "beautiful and joyous and robust and strong." Instead, he exalts—but without deep joy and often with a bitter pessimism—the benefactions of Production. In this way the viceroy of the universe runs the risk of becoming a lowly vassal of the things that serve him.

The first page of the Bible invites us to clear our eyes of the smoke with which an atheistic civilization has filled the world: it invites us to renew our minds, to savor the spiritual relish of earthly things, for *all things are good*. Above all, it invites us to rediscover in our joy and confident optimism traces of the Father who is the Maker of all beauty.

NOTES

1   The Babylonian poem of creation, *Enuma Elish*, is made up of seven fairly long tablets (125 to 160 verses). The original text has been lost; we know it through copies from Kish, Ashur, Ninive and Babylon. The most important collection of tablets, discovered at Ninive in 1948, belonged to the library of King Ashurbanipal. Cf J B Pritchard, *Ancient Near Eastern Texts* (= *A N E T*) (Princeton, 1950), 60.

2   Cf A Van der Voort, "Genèse, 1:1-2:4a, et le psaume 104," *R B* 58 (1951), 321-47.

3   The following is an outline of Chapter 1:

Prologue (vv 1-2): résumé and key					
Narrative proper (vv 3-31): two symmetrical periods of three days each:					
Day	Works	Ordering of	Appointments of	Works	Day
1st	1	Light is separated from darkness (day and night) (3-5)	Creation of the sun (for the day) and the moon and stars (for the night) (14-19)	5	4th
2nd	2	The two abysses (air and water) are separated (6-8)	Creation of the birds (for the air) and of fish (for the sea) (20-23)	6 ·	5th
3rd	3 4	Dry land separated from the watery areas (continent) and the production of the plants (9-13)	Creation of the animals and of man (24-31)	7 8	6th
Conclusion (2:1-3): the divine Worker rests					

4 According to Junker, *Die Biblische Urgeschichte* . . .
38 f, "The framework of seven days is simply an ideal
way of presenting the divine creation. The division
of time into weeks was sanctioned by ancient tradition and, as far as the Israelites were concerned, was
a law of the world established by God himself, who
ruled over the life and actions of man, and, consequently, the general course of the universe. . . . In
my opinion it would be false to admit that the obli-
gation of respecting the division into seven days and
the sabbath had no other foundation than the work
of the seven days. It was not because it was first
said 'God created the world in seven days,' that it
was then added, 'And so also man in his turn ought
to live and to work according to the division of time
into weeks.' On the contrary it was originally the
reverse; it was because man considered the week and
the sabbath a universal divine institution that God's
creative action was shown to be in conformity with
this division of time."

5 Various set phrases enter into the structure of the
couplets, those, namely, a) *of introduction*—"And God
said"; b) *of command*—"Let there be light"; c) *of exe-
cution*—"And it was so"; d) *of description*—"And God
separated the light"; e) *of blessing*—"God blessed," or
of naming—"And God called"; f) *of praise*—"And God
saw that it was good"; g) *of conclusion*—"And there
was evening and morning." A curious coincidence
may be noted in a correspondence between the different strophes of the narrative:

The arrows join the "strophes" containing the same
number of elements. It will be noted that the first
(vv 3-5) and the last (vv 26-31) contain the greatest

70

number, seven. Could this be a form of "inclusion"?
The fourth (vv 11-13) and the fifth (vv 14-19) strophes,
which form a sort of hinge for the two parts, are constructed in the same fashion, the elements found in
the same order.

Day	Work	Arrangement		Furnishing	Work	Day
1	1	a b c f d e g		a b c d f g	5	4
2	2	a b d c e g		a b d f e g	6	5
3	3	a b c e f		a b c d f	7	6
	4	a b c d f g		a b d e c f g	8	

6   "L'Age de la Terre," *Construire* 9 (1942), 192-194.
Cf Lecomte du Noüy, *L'Avenir de l'Esprit* (Paris,
1941), 139-78; *Human Destiny* (New York, 1947), 55 ff.

7   *Op* and *loc cit.*

8   The sacred author proceeded according to a definitely
schematic pattern. He schematized the setting, an
imaginary week, and the settlement of the universe,
and in ch 5 and 11, the genealogies. This literary
procedure is a characteristic of the document P.

9   P Dumaine "L'Heptaméron Biblique," *RB* 44 (1935),
164, note 2. The translation we propose remains uncertain.

10 T Moreaux, *Mon Curé chez les Savants*, 50.

11 "All that the sacred author asserts, enunciates, suggests must be held to be asserted, enunciated suggested by the Holy Ghost" (cf response of the Biblical
Commission, June 18, 1915). The same response for-
bids us to maintain that the Apostles, while not teaching any error, could nevertheless while under the inspiration of the Holy Ghost "express" personal and
human ideas which might be erroneous. "But," asks
Père Benoit, OP, "granted that God preserves his in-

terpreter from expressing an opinion which is erroneous in any way at all, even by implication, may it not be that the author without 'expressing' anything at all and in spite of himself, reveals his own personal views? The case is different. Here there is no question of an affirmation, however attenuated it might be (an 'implication' is still a voluntary and intentional mode of expression), but rather of a thought which is read only between the lines, outside the intention and against the will of the writer. It seems that this is possible and even inevitable" (*La Prophétie,* French translation of the *Summa Theologiae,* [*Revue des Jeunes,* Paris, 1947], 350). Cf Pesch, *De inspiratione Sacrae Scripture* (1906), 458, note 1; G. Courtade, "Inspiration et Inerrance," *V D B S* 4, 534 f.

11a As M J Lagrange, OP, points out (*R B* 5 [1896]), St. Thomas held that the treatment of creation by Genesis was not chronological but logical (*De Potentia,* q. 4, a 2, ad 2). It is for this reason that our explanation is called the "artistico-historical interpretation" of Genesis.

12 When the problem posed by the existence of the Cosmos and the Psyche was raised, the ancients, notwithstanding the promptings of their genius, were unable to give it the mysterious but necessary solution of a God-Creator. But once presented to the world, once it had been inspired and, as it were, "breathed" in from some other source, then reason became capable of discovering and demonstrating this solution without outside help. This is what took place among the philosophers rightly called Christian; faith intervened in their work only to the extent of making their reason more reasonable.

13 Nor is the author more definite about the origin of the stars. Such indifference on his part is in striking contrast to our modern concern, and should enlighten us as to the intention of the sacred writer.

14 It is not metaphysically impossible that a substance of an inferior order contain potentially a being of a higher order, and, certain conditions being verified, that it have passed from potency to act under the influence of a proportionate efficient cause. Now, insofar as there is question only of vital forms reducible to matter (ie, material forms), we cannot from the metaphysical point of view demand more than the efficiency of second causes. But the form or vital principle of plants and animals is precisely reducible to matter, on which it intrinsically depends for its being and action. Therefore, there is nothing which compels us to deny that the passage from the azoic to the vegetative order, and from the vegetative to the animal order can be effected from the original matter, it being pre-supposed that this matter possesses a suitable potency; and this could be affected under the influence solely of ordinary providence. Cf T J Motherway, SJ, *art cit;* Cyril Vollert, SJ, *art cit.*

15 F Ceuppens, O.P, *Genèse, I-III* (Paris, 1945), 33 f; *idem, Quaestiones Selectae ex Historia Primaeva* (Rome, 1947), 23 f.

16 St Gregory of Nyssa, *In Hexameron, P G* 44:701; St Augustine, *De Genesi ad Litteram,* Book 5: 4 and 5 *passim, P L* 34:323-327. On the interpretation of these texts see Boyer, *De Deo Creante* (Rome, 1933), 107 ff.

17 *Les grandes thèses de la philosophie thomiste,* 161; *S. Thomas d'Aquin* (Paris, 1922), 23. P Sertillanges,

OP, has repeated this same theme in one of his latest works, *L'Idée de Création,* ch. 6, "Création et évolution" (Paris, 1945). Cf N Luyten, O.P, "Philosophy and Evolution," *N Schol* 25 (1951), 290-312.

18 "In the great body of the world the divine murmur finds as many channels to come to us as there are creatures ruled by the divinity itself. Thus, when we look at everything that has been created, we are elevated to admiration for the Creator." St Gregory the Great, *Moralia,* 5:29; *P L* 75:727.

CHAPTER THREE

"Let Us Make Man In Our Image . . . ."

Not long ago the following paragraph appeared on the front page of a local newspaper.

MAN DESCENDED FROM AN APE

"Capetown, April 27, 1947.—Doctor Broom, anthropologist of the Pretoria Museum, has discovered a human skull in a cave at Sterkfontein (Transvaal). This skull, which according to him belonged to a woman in her fifties, definitely establishes the link between man and the anthropoid ape."

How did the readers of this item react to this sensational information? With indifference? With a skeptical smile? With conviction—or disquietude?

In any case the news once again brought before the public a question that has been hotly disputed for a century. How is it possible not to be moved by a question which has to do with our origin, and which concerns our destiny? Whether our modern horse has descended from the *Hyracotherium* or not, is of no interest to us. But are we the result of evolution? Do gorillas or chimpanzees figure among our ancestors? The answer to this exceptionally important question cannot leave thinking men indifferent.

At the beginning of our century, the slogan, "Man has descended from the apes," often reflected a materialistic frame of mind, and was a favorite weapon in the anti-religious arsenal. The air has been noticeably cleared since then. More and more Catholics, some of them university professors, have come out openly for a spiritualistic, teleological, theistic transformism. Nor are their ideas confined to the initiated, for they successively win over their own students and the Catholic elite, and then penetrate little by little into the popular mind.[1]

We shall not be so brash as to discuss on a scientific plane the often subtle conclusions of paleontologists, biologists and anthropologists. We simply state the fact that at the present moment most scientists, at least as a working hypothesis, hold for the animal origin of man's body. Exegetes and theologians should not ignore this fact or minimize its importance. On the contrary, they have an urgent duty to define as exactly as possible the *exigencies* and the *limits* of orthodoxy. In educated circles there is an evident desire for instruction, and along with this there is a sort of impatience, even a restiveness. There are some complaints of a lack of sufficient understanding on the part of those who are the "masters in Israel," who are accused by some of not being up-to-date, and of shutting themselves up in conservative positions as if these were impregnable fortresses. Many are now suffering crises of conscience because they cannot see how the new vision of the world suggested by science can be harmonized with the traditional teaching of the old Bible.

The following quotations, some of them lacking in moderation, bear this out.

"At the present time it is impossible, we believe, to recount sacred history as has been done in the past, insisting on the marvelous and treating as historical realities certain images which are the envelope of religious truths, as, for example, the creation of the woman from the rib of the man, or the eating of the forbidden fruit."

"To maintain that the text of Genesis reveals the order in which the species appeared, or the manner of creation, or the origin of the woman, would be to reduce this beautiful work of inspiration to primitive and infantile proportions."[2]

Some Catholics reproach the ecclesiastical authorities for their slowness:

"The impression is all too often given that she (the Church) rallies to the discoveries of genius with a monumental slowness, and that while waiting she allows men to go astray and perhaps lose their souls. The apostasy of one soul from among the elite may well be the remote cause of a general apostasy. Is it not desirable that theologians take up the problems of their contemporaries, instead of basking lazily in the tranquil possession of the truth? In theology, as in other fields, dogmatic slumber is not a guarantee of truth, nor even of fidelity to tradition."[3]

Among the causes of the modern unbelief may be singled out the "reprehensible attitude of too many Catholics, especially clerics, in regard to certain scientific theories. It would seem that the Church compels us to place ourselves in definite camps; that we cannot be good Catholics if we hold certain hypotheses to which excellent Catholics subscribe and which Rome has never condemned. . . . One of the objections raised against religion a few years back by a professor in a woman's college was that the priests were unable to reconcile the Scriptures with the theory of evolution."[4]

The dilemma of a Catholic scientist may be stated as follows: "The origin of the human body by way of evolution does not appear to be at all improbable. Many or almost all anthropologists hold that a genetic and physical connection with lower living beings is not only a well-founded supposition, but even a reality.

78

We think that it is a serious hypothesis, and that it has
some basis in fact. We turn to the theologians to ask
if our opinion regarding the origin of the human body
is compatible with Catholic doctrine. They have taught
us that God took dust from the earth and from it
formed the first man. We moderns question the interpretation of these words and ask: Did God form the
body of man *immediately* from the dust, or from some
organic matter prepared by him by a long teleological
evolution? Is such an opinion compatible with the divine teaching? What exactly did God reveal? Did he
reveal that the body of man came *directly* from the
dust, or is this a human interpretation? The doubts
of those of us who believe will vanish if we are given
the true meaning of the word of God, and we will go
on in the certainty that science, which today is uncertain, will tomorrow shed light on the origin of the
human body *in harmony with the divine word.* But if
the theologians do not yet know the true meaning of
the revelation, let them not impose upon us a burden
which many may not be able to bear. Their responsibility is indeed great, but their mission is also sub-
lime."[5]

"It is certain that for a long time the Church has
looked with anything but favor upon a doctrine, Transformism, which from its very beginning, particularly
because of the anti-Christian use to which some of its
adherents put it, seemed to attack some of the essential
points of Catholic or even theistic doctrine. Later

modifications of the original ideas by the scientists—among whom there are some Churchmen of note—and by the philosophers, call for a new consideration of the problem. This is the hope of many theologians and scientists at present."[6]

This "reconsideration" demands both reserve and prudence, for the question of origins involves a great deal of theology. If man did not appear spontaneously in the world like a flower thrust into a bouquet; if on the contrary he was fashioned slowly within the animal nature, if he blossomed like a flower on its stem, one naturally will ask if humanity began with one or several couples—a serious problem which we shall consider at length in the following chapter. On the other hand, how can the ideal state of our first parents as described for us in our text-books of theology be reconciled with the reconstruction of "primitive" man attempted by the naturalists?

"Did the author of Genesis think that humanity in its entirety descended from a single couple? An unbiased reading of the book seems to lead to the conclusion that, in his eyes, all men living on earth are the descendants of the first sinful couple whose names were Adam and Eve. So the matter was understood by Christian antiquity, and this stand on the matter is binding upon Catholics of today as a standard of belief. Recent discoveries in the field of anthropology and biology have, however, led some scientists to propose the *theory of polygenism*, that is, of the existence of several distinct stocks at the origin of humanity, whether it be an existing or a pre-historic humanity. Still only a hypothesis, this view has not won anything like unanimous acceptance by even non-believing scientists.

"It is noteworthy that a question which believers have up to now considered as proper to revelation should be transferred to the scientific realm, and be freely discussed in relation to observed facts. . . . New perspectives of which centuries of Christian thought had no inkling have been opened up to us, and invite us to read the old book with more attentive eyes."[7]

These remarks, chosen at random from many made by priests and laymen, reflect the concern of our contemporaries. The laity urges exegetes and theologians on, presses them to go ahead, to abandon a too-literal interpretation of the Bible account, to re-think the traditional doctrines .

As is only to be expected, such requests precipitate very different reactions in theological circles. On the one side there is a reserve in regard to what is termed the evolutionist craze, a mistrust of Catholic "progressives," a consolidation of acquired positions; on the other, audacious suggestions which are irreconcilable with data considered to be sacrosanct. Aroused by the excesses of a few, ecclesiastical authority has intervened to calm the legitimate anxiety of her children and to make its directives more precise. The encyclical *Humani Generis* only recently established the limits and conditions under which Catholic scientists may freely discuss these points.

It is of prime importance that we distinguish the truths of the faith and certain conclusions of theology, from the perhaps debatable conclusions of theologians, the certain from the uncertain, the probable from the possible, the fundamental and unchanging sense of the text from the facile and worthless explanations to which in the course of centuries this account has given rise. Discriminating care must guide the exegete or theologian when he takes up the many questions regarding the origin of man. When was man born and where? How did he come in the world? How many representatives of the human race were there, in the beginning? What was the primitive state of men?

Let us look into the principal, the most delicate question of all: how did man make his appearance in the world? The solution of most of the other problems hinges upon it.

I

The Bible tells the story of our beginning twice. The first account we have already seen: *God (Elohim) said: Let us make mankind in our image and likeness; and let them have dominion over the fish of the sea, the birds of the air, the cattle, over all the wild animals and every creature that crawls on the earth.*

*God (Elohim) created man in his image
In the image of God (Elohim) he created him.
Male and female, he created them.*

*God (Elohim) saw that all he had made was very
good. And there was evening and morning, the sixth
day.*

* * * * *

Man is thus portrayed as the last actor to enter
upon the scene of the world, an arrangement called
for by the plan of the narrator. Was he concerned
with chronology? According to scientists, man *was* the
last being in the series to appear, so that in actual fact
the teaching of the Bible here coincides with the findings of science. We hold, however, that the sacred
author was not the least bit interested in teaching
anything about the chronological order. His attention
was directed elsewhere. He intended to instill a religious teaching in the minds of his readers, to draw
from the world its essential meaning, and to bring out
the hierarchy existing in God's works. At the summit
of the scale of beings stood man, who by the perfection
of his nature was to dominate the universe. It was for
him that the heavens and the earth and their armies
exist.

"It was not proper," remarked Saint Gregory of
Nyssa, "that the chief should make his appearance before his subjects. The king should logically be revealed
only after his kingdom had been readied for him,

when the Creator of the universe had, so to say, prepared a throne for him who was to rule. Then did God cause man to appear in the world, to be both a contemplater of the marvels of the universe, and the master. . . . Man was last to be created, not that he should therefore be contemptuously relegated to the last place, but because from his very birth it was fitting that he be king of his domain."[8]

This idea of the primacy of man is the spiritual inheritance of mankind,[9] and stands out in sharp relief in the setting chosen by the sacred writer. The divine workman consistently worked from what is imperfect to what is more perfect. When he had created man, and only then, he said that everything was *very* good. We might almost say that God was "improvising" throughout the preceding creations, and that before proceeding to create our nature he reflected and deliberated. "The sun is created; that required no deliberation. The same holds true for the heavens. There is nothing like them in creation, yet a single word sufficed to produced them. But deliberation proceded the formation of man; according to the Scriptures the Creator first drew up a plan and then said: Let us make mankind in our image."[10]

* * * * *

This text (Gen 1:26) often has been compared with fragments of the Assyro-Babylonian literature. In the *Poem of Creation,* for example, Marduk decides to create an artistic work, man. He deliberates within himself: "Blood will I mass and cause bones to be, and to establish a human being, whose name shall be man. I wish to create the human being, man." According to other traditions the goddess Mami fashioned the human features "in her image"; and the divinity Aruru formed Eabani "in the image of the god Anu."

Did the sacred author adapt to monotheism and insert in his own account an older formula which was the heritage of the Assyro-Babylonian civilization?[11] There is no need to be scandalized at such a question. Do not Christian orators often intersperse their sermons with references to the Greek and Latin classics? This hypothesis might easily explain the presence of the plural form, "Let *us* make man in *our* image and likeness."

To exalt the creation of man the sacred author adopted a new literary artifice and depicted Elohim as taking counsel with the mysterious beings who made up his court before proceeding to decisive act.[12]

❋   ❋   ❋   ❋   ❋

Superior to the animals, endowed with an intellect and will, man resembles his Creator; he is his ikon, his earthly effigy. No need to assign two distinct meanings to *image* and *likeness* (cf Gen 5:1-3); the redundance simply suggests that man is a very good image, without implying an out and out identification with God. Saint Irenaeus was the first to treat of *image* as

85

a natural likeness, and *likeness* as a supernatural one.[13] In imitation of the Creator, man exercises a delegated overlordship over all the animals of the earth. He is truly the "animal who commands," as Saint Gregory of Nyssa used to say. From this we can understand why the psalmist, meditating on the first page of the Bible, gave so fervent an expression to his admiration and acknowledgment:

What is man that you should be mindful of him,
Or the son of man that you should care for him?
You have made him little less than the angels *('elohim)*.

The narrator of Genesis, though apparently not attuned to the mood of the poet, reveals his enthusiasm in his own way. His sentences become breathless and he breaks the rhythm:

And God (Elohim) created man in his image,
In the image of God (Elohim), he created him.
Male and female he created them.

Psalm 8 helps bring our commentary on the creation narrative into sharper focus. It insinuates that God has created man not only in his image, but also in the image of the *'elohim*, heavenly spirits whom the Bible sometimes describes as surrounding the throne of God.[14] Being thus created after God has deliberated with the angels, man resembles both the Creator and the celestial spirits. He is a veritable microcosm recapitulating in himself the **divine** world, "And God (Elohim) created him in his image"; the **angelic** world,

"in the image of the *'elohim* he created him"; and the
animal world, "male and female he created them."

As some exegetes have remarked, the sacred writer
makes separate mention of the distinction into sexes,
and declares fecundity to be a special blessing. The
generative power, therefore, is not a part of the likeness of God. The author perhaps intended thus to
point out in a somewhat veiled manner, and as a re-
buke to pagan perversions, that it is not by sex that
man realizes the divine image. Lecomte du Noüy errs
in assuming this text to be a "quasi-symbolical and
cryptic description of scientific truths," thinking to see
in it the appearance of the "first as yet unconscious
human form," still the slave of instincts and physiological functions, but on its way to consciousness and
freedom.[15] The sacred writer does, it is true, use strictly physiological terms like "male and female" and notes
the command to increase and multiply. His purpose
is clear: he wants to show that sex is a good thing
and that it is something made by God. But in his eyes
this sexual being which is related to the animals also
bears a resemblance to God, in that he is already
possessed of consciousness and freedom.

The author does not describe this marvelous creation but simply announces it as a fact. **He attempts
no historical precision.** With only this text before us
we could even believe that God with one act produced
the man and the woman. Whether in so doing he
made use of pre-existing matter or not, the text does

not say. Moreover, strictly speaking, *from this text* it is impossible to solve the question of the number of the first representatives of the human species, whether there was a single couple or many primitive couples. The *text* sustains either hypothesis.

Recall the hagiographer's description of the origin of the land animals: "Let the earth bring forth all kinds of living creatures: cattle, crawling creatures, and wild animals. . . . And God (Elohim) made all kinds of wild beasts, every kind of cattle, every kind of creature crawling on the ground." All these terms, *wild beasts, cattle, crawling creatures*, are collective terms. Immediately afterwards, on the same sixth day, the sacred author records the creation of man. Does he modify his vocabulary? Not at all. "Let us make mankind," declares the Creator. Here again a collective term is used; God proposes to create the human species, and the verb that follows is put in the plural:[16] "*Let them have dominion* over the fish of the sea, and the birds of the air." Strictly speaking, then, from the first chapter of Genesis *alone* we could maintain that the human race was represented in the beginning by a number of individuals.[17] But there is only a single human species; the animals appeared according to their many species. When it is a question of man the narrator changes his formula and insists on the distinction of sexes: "male and female he created them."

The certain teaching of this first chapter may now be briefly summarized:

1. Man owes his existence to the special intervention of God.

2. Man, the image of his Creator, is endowed with a nature that sets him in a place apart, elevates him above the animals, and makes of him the master of the visible universe.

3. There is only one single human species.

4. Man was created male and female, in order that the human race might be propagated by the union of the sexes, according to the divine command.

5. Despite their difference in sex, both the man and the woman are like unto God.

Aside from these points, much uncertainty remains. When did this special intervention of God take place? How much time elapsed between the formation of the world and the appearance of man? How many human beings were there? Where was the human race first cradled?

The first creation-account leaves these questions unanswered. For further information, then, we turn to the second account.

II

When the Lord God (Yahweh Elohim) made the earth and the heavens, there was not yet any field shrub on the earth nor had the plants of the field sprung up, for the Lord God (Yahweh Elohim) had sent no rain on the earth and there was no man to till the soil; but a mist [or a stream] rose from the earth and watered all the surface of the ground. Then the Lord God (Yahweh Elohim) formed man out of the dust of the ground and breathed into his nostrils the breath of life, and man became a living being . . .

Then the Lord God (Yahweh Elohim) said: 'It is not good that the man is alone; I will make him a helper like himself.'

So, the Lord God (Yahweh Elohim) had formed out of the ground all the beasts of the field and the birds of the air. He brought them to the man to see what he would call them; for that which the man called each of them would be its name. The man named all the cattle, all the birds of the air and all the beasts of the field; but he found no helper like himself.

The Lord God (Yahweh Elohim) cast the man into a deep sleep, and while he slept, took one of his ribs and closed up its place with flesh. And the rib which the Lord God (Yahweh Elohim) took from the man, he made into a woman, and brought her to him.

Then the man said:
  'She is now bone of my bone
  And flesh of my flesh;
  She shall be called Woman,
    For from man she has been taken.'

For this reason a man leaves his father and mother, and clings to his wife; and the two become one flesh.

One need not be profoundly versed in the secrets of literary criticism to notice the profound differences between this and the preceding account. The first is dogmatic, with broad, stylized outline; the second is colorful, picturesque, realistic. In the former we hear a theologian giving a lecture—adapted to his audience, to be sure, but still unmistakably intellectual in tone. In the latter it is a popular teacher who speaks. In the first narrative Elohim gives orders, "Let this or that be done." In the second we see God himself taking a hand in the work. Like a potter, he molds a lump of clay, he forms the animals, he breathes into the nostrils of the man, he organizes a parade of the animals; he extracts one of the man's ribs, fills up the cavity with flesh, and builds the rib into a woman. In both, there is the same God, the Creator; but in the second account he is humanized, condescending, a familiar kind of God who is in turn a potter, a gardener, and a "surgeon" (2: 7, 19, 8, 21). Here for the first time the Bible calls the Lord by his own proper name, Yahweh, or "He-who-is." Here, as before, the attention of the narrator is focused principally on the creation of the man and the woman. But in order to emphasize the primacy of man, the author has changed the plot.

A complete description of this new narration would involve an examination of its characteristic vocabulary and style, and we leave that task to the specialists. It is enough for us to retain the conclusion reached by the literary critics, namely, that the same hand did not write the two accounts. The first is the learned adaptation of a theologian; the second, a lesson full of imagery given by a popular teacher.

A summary description precedes the creation of the man: "There was not yet any field shrub on the earth, nor had the plants of the field sprung up."[18] In other words, the earth was deprived of ornamentation such as wild plants and vegetables, and resembled a desert. Why? Because "the Lord God (Yahweh Elohim) had sent no rain on the earth, and there was no man to till the soil." That is, there was no water to moisten the soil nor any man to irrigate and work it.

This apparently banal reflection tends less to furnish us with a chronological reference than it does to teach us man's role in nature.[19] Strictly speaking, rain by itself would suffice for the growth of shrubs. But without man-power, and—in Palestine especially—without labor and continual irrigation, how could the soil produce grain and vegetables? The earth has as much need of man as of the rain from heaven. God remedies the dryness of the soil, causing a stream (or mist) to rise out of the earth. River or mist, it matters little; from now on there will be water for irrigating the land.

The Creator then proceeded to make man, and the manner in which the event is recounted brings out the grandeur of this priviliged creature. As a potter will mold a lump of clay, so God fashions the human body. Then he breathed a breath of life into the man's nostrils. And the molded clay became a living person.

Long ago Saint Augustine warned the reader to be on his guard against any naive notions that this narrative might bring to mind. How childish to believe that with his own hands God fashioned the body of the man out of the clay of the earth, and to suppose that the Creator exhaled a very material breath out of his own lungs. God has neither hands nor lungs. Such realistic images, however, propose this profound truth, that man and everything about him is linked with God.[20]

* * * * *

Not being philosophically-minded, the Hebrews had not speculated on the constitutive principle of man, nor had they scientifically analyzed the elements which make up the human body. But they had noticed that after death the body disintegrates and vanishes into dust, and from this naturally concluded that *earth* entered into man's composition. Yet in addition to this material element there is life in man, and it is manifested by his breathing. We define man as a rational animal; the Hebrews would have defined him as "dust that breathes."

Just as in the first account the author told of the origin of the universe in accordance with the scientific notions of his times, in the second the sacred historian pictures the creation of man according to his own ideas of what man was made of. To bring out the fact of the divine intervention to his contemporaries, the sacred writer pictured two scenes for them.

In the first scene Yahweh is portrayed as a potter who with his fingers kneads and molds the clay. With this concept the Hebrews were familiar, for in Egypt, the land of their exile, they had known forced-labor in "clay and brick." In addition, the image was a traditional one. In the land of Sumer, the potter-goddess Mami took seven lumps of clay, out of which she made seven men, and seven more for seven women. According to some of the Babylonian texts, man was created by the god Ea, who was in Sumerian the "potter god." In Egypt it was Khnum who modeled man on a potter's-wheel. Common "scientific" notions underlie common images.

The second scene completes the first. Yahweh Elohim breathes his own breath into the nostrils of man. Here again experience played its part. Breath is a sign of life; at death, one "breathes" his last. The sacred author could find no more provocative an image than this to teach that God is the author of life.[21]

God, therefore, stands at the origin of man, of every man. As a material being, he receives his body from Yahweh Elohim; as a living being, he receives his very life's breath from Yahweh Elohim.

But what, then, of man's privileged position? The animals too were made by God out of the slime of the earth, and received the breath of life from the Creator, as our author states in so many words: "The Lord God (Yahweh Elohim) had formed out of the ground all the beasts of the field and the birds of the air." As for the breath of life: "(I will bring the flood upon the earth so as to destroy from under heaven) all flesh in which there is the breath of life" (Gen 6:17; 7:15): "All (men and animals) that were on the dry land, in whose nostrils was the breath of life, died" (Gen 7:22).[22] The psalmist shared the same idea: "If you take away their breath, they perish. . . . When you send forth your spirit (breath), they are created, and you renew the face of the earth" (Ps 104:29-30). Indeed, "all things (man and beast) breathe alike" (Eccles 3:19).

To all this we may say "Yes and No." Yes, because like the animal man is a "dust that breathes," and like the animal, he has his origin from God; both were formed by God. No, because unlike the beasts of the field and the birds of the air, man is a "dust that thinks"; he is capable of knowing the nature of animals

(Gen 2:19-20) and is the master of his destiny (Gen 3). He is a privileged creature, and on this score deserves the attention of the narrator. By a very special setting the author shows us that man, and only man, was the object of a *particular intervention* on the part of God, and by it was made to be a material being, a living being, a thinking and a free being.

How are we to picture this divine intervention as taking place? Philosophy helpfully completes what the text suggests by proving that a being endowed with thought and freedom, such as is the man described in Genesis, has an immaterial soul. Hence, the divine intervention which vivified the "dust of the earth" had by that very act to create the soul of the first man. The special act of God, symbolized by his "in-breathing," was in reality a true creation. Thus the divine gesture is given its full significance: the human soul, a spiritual substance, comes immediately from God. The sacred author could hardly have expressed the word "soul" better than by using "breath" as its image. In all languages the etymology of the word "soul" (spirit, Geist, etc) bears this out.

It is much more difficult to picture the divine operation by which the human body was formed. It is generally agreed that imagery plays a notable part in the description given in Genesis. "No modern theologian interprets the text of Genesis literally, as if God had molded earth so as to form the human body. The clay statue, first molded into the human form and then

animated by the breath of the Creator, most certainly
has no defenders today. In his day Saint Augustine
warned Christians to be on their guard against too
slavish an interpretation of this text, wherein symbolical expressions abound. He also told them to be careful about accepting things that would seem ridiculous
to unbelievers."[23]

What historical reality lies behind the formation
of man's body? Many authors maintain that, the anthropomorphisms being properly understood, *God created man's body directly from inorganic matter.* These
authors do not attempt any imaginative reconstruction
of the operation. They merely state that, by an act of
His all-powerful will, God simply caused, out of "the
primordial earth and the primordial clay," that matter
which Adam's soul was to animate, thus avoiding the
twofold danger of over-literalism, and of evolutionism,
which theory they are not inclined to accept.

Other theologians and exegetes approach the text
in the light of recent biological and paleontological discoveries, for they feel that the first chapter of Genesis
was given a satisfactory explanation by utilizing the
progress made in the field of geology. By his omnipotence, then, according to these authors, *God drew
the human body* not from inorganic matter but *from
an animal organism,* which he transformed and adapted so as to receive a human soul. "The (sacred) author
does not say that, following the infusion of a human
soul, the body of the first man, which had been

formed out of the dust of the ground by God, became a living thing from a non-living thing, but that it became a "living person" (the Hebrew text); in other words, human life was communicated to it. This body, primitively formed out of the dust of the earth, may therefore have already had a sub-human life when God, taking this already living being, may have made it a living person by infusing a soul into it."[24]

Many advance more boldly along this path at the risk, sometimes, of concealing the special action of God from superficial readers. As in the preceding hypothesis, they have recourse to the vagueness of the sacred text, or to the theory of "sudden mutations" now so much in vogue. Concretely, they propose that the human body came into being at the end of an erratic series of sudden mutations, each increasingly richer, and directed to this end by Providence. These directed mutations reveal the plan of the Creator, and are scattered along the long road which leads to man. At the last stage a "sudden progressive mutation may have produced a more perfect state, occasioning the creation and infusion of the human soul."[25] In order to mold this human organism God used many natural activities as so many "hands" or *instruments* of his power. Left to themselves these activities would most certainly not tend to produce what their nature did not require, nor could they terminate as the result of a series of haphazard mutations in the wondrously complex human body. But if these natural activities were prompted from within by a God who is always present to his creation and who, as Saint Augustine so beautifully says, incessantly mingles with his works, could not those very natural activities produce the mutations which prepared the matter for the last disposition necessary for the blossoming of the soul?[26] The scientist on his *experimental* plane notes only a variation or an explosion of nature, a new threshhold over which life steps in its forward progress. But the philosopher and theologian discern, on the *ontological* plane, the special action of the Creator.

*   *   *   *   *

What shall be said of such theories? All of them fit into the teaching of the Church, for they safeguard the *particular creation of man,* singled out by the Biblical Commission as being one of the historical facts which touch upon the very foundations of our faith. All three **hypotheses** recognize a special intervention on the part of God in the formation of the human body: God transforms inorganic matter, or causes an animal organism to undergo some change, or elevates the natural activities of sub-human living beings—yet none of these interpretations obliges us to accept it.

"Man became a **living person.**" This translation is correct, and can be found in the Hebrew lexicon. The advantage of it is that it leaves a door open for the evolutionists. Before becoming a living person by the divine breath, the matter used by the Creator *may* have already been a living organism.

It is equally possible that "dust of the earth" refers to a body originally formed from the slime of the earth, although that is not the obvious meaning. But one may ask whether in this popular account the author intended to affirm what we attribute to him. After all, he had written, "The dust of the earth, animated by the breath of Yahweh, became a *living soul*," and this is transposed into "A living organism, animated by the breath of Yahweh, became a *living person.*" Can this be an insidious infiltration, the last gasp of concordism?

Are we then to fall back upon the so-called traditional interpretation? Its partisans rightly set aside the strict meaning of the Hebrew verb used to describe the divine action. God did not "fashion" anything out of clay; this they recognize for the metaphor that it is. The inspired author understood the difficult task of expressing a divine reality for rather simple minds, of compiling a history whose peculiar material lay outside the field of experience, for no man was present at creation, with camera in hand. Guided by the spirit of God, the narrator used a literary device and modeled his description of God's activity on the human actions of a potter. Before a human artisan works his clay he must dig it out of the ground, and then, as he works it, he fashions it. Yahweh therefore also assembled his material, *the dust of the earth,* and then fashioned it into man.

But if the actual molding of the clay is a metaphor, as all agree, may not the material that is molded likewise be a metaphor? Might not the "dust of the earth" be a metaphor which was admirably suited to the scene? The essential thing is that "God formed the body of man in a special way." But what is meant by the "body of man?" Clearly not something composed of oxygen, hydrogen, carbon, nitrogen, but a material, perishable, and apparently earthly substance, a "quintessence of dust." As Père Lagrange once wrote, "The dust stands for the material element of the human composite."[27]

It would however be a mistake to stress the *earthly* origin of the human body; emphasis should be placed upon its *divine* origin, and not so much upon its *origin* as upon the earthly **nature** of this human body. We moderns are so influenced by the scientific work of our times that we have misplaced the central point of interest.

We agree with Professor H Junker, who writes: "The biblical account does not intend to teach us the material phases of Adam's creation, and does not tell us *how* man was created, but *that* he was created. Its peculiar doctrinal content is made up of truths concerning the nature of man and his relation to God. The literary form of the exposition symbolically dramatizes these truth."[28]

We may, therefore, consider the following teachings of this second account as **certain**:

1. By his body man is related to the earth; we may call him earthly, earthy, earthsome.

2. A privileged creature by reason of his soul, man is related to his Creator, and by his soul is immediately and directly joined to him. Moreover, the Bible, which presents the first man as endowed with an intellect and as master of his own fate, furnishes us with the elements which permit us to conclude to the strict creation of the human soul,[29] a creative act implied in the metaphor of breathing.

3. Man's body also comes from God. The Bible does not go into the precise origin of the human body, and there is some uncertainty here. Was it by creation? By the transformation of inorganic matter? By the reorganization of a pre-existing organism? The Bible maintains its neutrality.[30]

In a discourse uttered on November 30, 1941 in the presence of the members of the Pontifical Academies, Pope Pius XII summarized these certainties and uncertainties. After calling to mind the narrative of Genesis, the Pontiff enumerated several incontestable truths, among them man's creation in the image of God, and the essential superiority given to him over the animals by reason of his spiritual soul, thus excluding the hypothesis of the purely animal origin of the man and the woman. "The multiple researches of biology, paleontology and morphology on other problems touching the origin of man have not, up to the present, terminated in anything positively clear and certain. We must leave to the future the answer to the question, if science, enlightened and guided by revelation, will some day be able to give certain and definitive results on so important a matter."[31]

Pius XII broached the same subject again in his encyclical *Humani Generis:* "For these reasons the Teaching Authority of the Church does not forbid that, in conformity with the present state of human sciences and sacred theology, research and discussions by men experienced in both fields be pursued in regard to the doctrine of evolution, insofar as it inquires into the origin of the human body as coming from pre-existent living matter—for the Catholic faith obliges us to hold that souls are immediately created by God. However, this must be done in such a way that the reasons for both opinions, that is, those favorable and unfavorable to evolution, be weighed and judged with the necessary seriousness, moderation and measure, and provided that all are prepared to submit to the judgment of the Church, to whom Christ has given the mission of interpreting authentically the Sacred Scriptures and of defending the dogmas of faith.[32] Some, however, rashly transgress this liberty of discussion, acting as if the origin of human from pre-existing and living matter were absolutely certain and now proved by what has been discovered and by what has been drawn from these facts, as if there were nothing in

103

the sources of divine revelation which might here impose the greatest moderation and caution."[33]

III

When dealing with problems of human origins we often merely repeat the story, and comment on the creation *of the man, Adam.* There is here a conscious or unconscious attempt to minimize the problem, for there were *two* "men." "Then the Lord God (Yahweh Elohim) said, 'It is not good for man to be alone.' "

Thus begins a description which has often been treated with derision by unbelievers. And indeed the story lends itself readily to derision, considering the over-literal commentaries that have been made on the theme of Adam's rib. Did God take a rib with flesh on it? Had the Creator, foreseeing what he would do, provided Adam with an extra rib? Or did he exchange the rib which was removed for another, a spare one? Serious teachers both ancient and modern have attempted to satisfy our curiosity on these points.[34]

The account of the woman's creation definitely annoys many of our contemporaries. All the more reasons, then, for our not passing it over in silence.

Recent solutions to this problem reveal a decided trend towards a **mitigated realism.** The rib itself is soft-pedalled, and it is simply stated that God formed the body of the first woman using matter taken from the body of the man. It has been noticed that the "term which we translate as *rib* or *side* is one of the most obscure words of Genesis,"[35] chosen perhaps "as a symbol to indicate the identical nature of both the man and the woman."[36] By a curious coincidence the same sign, TI, in the Sumerian language has the double meaning of *life* and *rib*, a fact which seems to indicate that there was some connection between the ideas of life and rib which prompted the use of the rib as a symbol of the life force.[37]

According to this system of mitigated realism, the woman issued **physically** from the body of the first man. The common opinion assumes that this called for a miracle of God's omnipotence, and that it was carried out independently of secondary causes. Some theologians, however, see another solution within an evolutionary framework: "If the world has indeed followed the law of evolution, we may perhaps eventually find an explanation of some kind for the natural origin of the woman who has come from the man. We should therefore go very carefully here, and not rashly offer solutions to this question. **Reserving the last word on this subject to the judgment of the Church,** we conclude that there is no cogent reason why we should at the present time abandon the more commonly received explanation which asserts the miraculous origin of the woman from the first man."[73a]

Some theologians propose a concrete solution for the origin of the body of the woman just as they did for the body of the man, holding that the interpretation of the biblical text would perhaps be still easier in the transformist hypothesis of the sudden mutation of two individuals, in that the mutation of the female might have been induced by the male.

How strange to find that concordism still exercises its charm today!

Some exegetes apply an historico-idealistic explanation to this difficult text, looking upon the biblical description as a **historical parable,** and for this view some support may be found in Cajetan. "The text and context," wrote that eminent Dominican, "constrain me to interpret the formation of the woman not according to the letter (*non ut sonat littera*), nor even after the manner of an allegory, but as a mysterious parable (*secundum mysterium non allegoriae, sed parabolae*)."[38]

What mysterious historical reality lies hidden behind that parable?

*   *   *   *   *

Before creating the first woman, Yahweh deliberated with himself: "It is not good for man to be alone." Left alone, man is not sufficient for himself, and as he especially needs a companion and a helper for the propagation of the species, the Lord decided to "make him a helper like himself."

We would ordinarily expect God to carry out his plan at once, but instead he set about creating the beasts of the field and the birds of the air, and then

PARADISE a Supernatural
atmosphere for man
TREE OF LIFE
                    INNER LAW
                    OF MIND

" " good + evil
                    LOWER PART
                    OF MAN — SENSE

SERPENTS DARTING tongue
8 212

The LORD GOD
phanted a garden
in Eden,
to the east.
A privehleged phace
which GOD
in His bounty
had prepared
for the first mankind

caused them to pass before the solitary man. The narrator thus dramatically comes back to the theme of the divine deliberation: "I will make him a helper like himself." The man reviews the animals of creation, he notes their natures, and then imposes names on them. He becomes aware of his superiority to them, and consequently of the impossibility of finding among them a *helper proper to him as man.*

This picturesque scene directly prepares the reader for what follows. Like a practiced surgeon, Yahweh Elohim induces his patient to sleep. "The *Lord* God (Yahweh Elohim) cast the man into a deep sleep and, while he slept, took one of his ribs and closed up its place with flesh. And the rib which the *Lord* God (Yahweh Elohim) took from the man he made into a woman, and brought her to him." Then, overjoyed, the man sang the first hymn of conjugal love: "She now is bone of my bone, and flesh of my flesh." A moment ago the man had found no companion among all the living things that peopled the earth and the sky, but that situation has now been changed.

When God presented the first woman to him, the man gave voice to his joy in lyical tones. "This time" he has met his "helpmeet!" "Bone of my bone and flesh of my flesh."[39] And immediately, for every being needs a name, the man, who as master had already designated the animals by their names, imposed upon the woman a name expressive of her nature: "She shall be called *Woman,* for from *man* she has been taken. For

107

this reason a man leaves his father and mother, and clings to his wife, and the two become one flesh."

The mysterious attraction of the sexes is rooted in their nature. The bonds of monogamous marriage bind a man to his wife with a bond even stronger than the ties of blood. The two together now form but the one flesh. The breaking of the sacred bond of marriage is thus as unthinkable as to separate the members from their common body. This is the primitive plan promulgated under the inspiration of the Holy Ghost by either the first man or by the sacred author himself.

The doctrinal depth of these few lines holds the reader spellbound. One need not be a great scholar to see how revolutionary such a teaching was in the ancient pagan world. "The man and woman form a unity; both share a common nature which is superior to all animal nature, and because intelligent, they can think and talk. However, they complement one another, for both do not have the same aptitudes. The man came first; the woman was created as his companion and helper. The man will love the woman as a part of himself, and the woman will love the man as her support, the leader upon whom she depends."[40]

*   *   *   *   *

The double account of the creation of the man and the formation of the woman has been edited by the same hand. In both cases, at the start of the description a point is made: in one, that the earth without man is doomed to sterility (2:5); in the second, that without the woman the man lacks an indispensable complement (2:18). In both cases, the creation of the man and formation of the woman fitted in logically with the formation of the other beings: in the first with the appearance of vegetative life (2:5), in the second with that of the animals (2:19). The parallel is a good one, clearly highlighting the idea of the hierarchy which exists throughout God's creation.

Both accounts involve a play on words. In the first the name of the man, Adam, evokes the word for earth, *'adamah.* In such an assonance the readers would grasp a twofold truth: one part of man is material and perishable and he is "dust of the earth"; in addition he is bound "to till and keep the earth" (2:7, 15), he is earthy, he owns land. In the second account, the name for woman derives by popular etymology from the word for husband, *'ishah, 'ish;* bride, groom; wife, husband. It is a clear affirmation of their identity in nature, and an unequivocal proclamation that it is woman's destiny to help and to complement her husband (2:18) in the unity of "one flesh" (2:24).

To carry the parallel further, both cases constitute a kind of **historical parable.** In the first the narrator tells of man's coming upon the world-scene—a unique event, the first fact of human history. To make this singular history live again, he drew from his store of traditional oriental imagery the metaphors of the potter and the clay, the dust of the earth, and breathing, and through such literary devices succeeded in evoking before our eyes the figure of man who was the king of creation and God's masterpiece.

One might expect that an author, setting out to complete the first history, would have made use of the same literary devices in both accounts.[41] In both cases the same truth was to be illustrated, a teaching which had to do with man's nature and with the fact that by it he is a *material* and a *spiritual being*, that as such he comes from God; and that by her nature the woman is *of the same nature as the man*, is dependent upon him, forms with him one single moral person; her very being comes from God also.

Since one of these panels of the diptych is done in imaged history, why could not the second also be so done?

* * * * *

It is often asserted that the second creation account (2:4-25) takes up again, so as to complete and clarify it, the outline sketched in the first chapter. The second may perhaps have embellished the first with the addition of its own proper imagery, but that it added any historical detail is not so certain. Let us see for ourselves.

110

First Account 1:27	Second Account 2:7, 21-22
And Elohim created man.	*And Yahweh formed man, dust of the earth.*
Here the verb expressing the divine action is part of a theological vocabulary. It is a technical term. It designates the divine action in the proper sense. It does not evoke any image. In sum, it is an abstract word.	The verb here also belongs to a technical vocabulary, but it is not the technical language of the theologian. It is borrowed from the art of pottery. *Yatsar* expresses the art of the potter molding his clay. In sum, it is a concrete word.

In both texts it is affirmed that God produced man by a special operation. This then is the real, historical fact. But the second account adds something by introducing the new image of the potter; it is the beginning of a parable. The new image does not embellish the story, but it does throw some light on the essential fact of the first account.

First Account	Second Account
And Elohim created man in his image.	*And he breathed into his nostrils the breath of life.*
According to the first account man might be defined as "an image made in the likeness of God." An abstract definition.	The second account describes rather than defines man; Adam is "a dust that breathes." A descriptive definition.

111

The two accounts agree in this particular, that in man there is something divine. Adam by God's will is a combination of matter and life; God so created him. This is the real historical fact.[42] But the second account introduces a new item in the breath of Yahweh Elohim, a detail which adds nothing to the historical fact. The first account appeals to the mind, the second to the imagination. The fact is then enriched by an image.

First Account	Second Account
Male and female he created them.	*And the rib which Yahweh Elohim took from the man he made into a woman.*
God created the sexes in the beginning. Being of the same species, man and woman are mutually complementary.	The woman, of the same nature as the man, was created to be a help-mate for the man; she is a "fit" companion for him.

In both accounts here one great fact is clear: God stands at the origin of the sexes. He it was who created the man and the woman, the latter being man's natural complement. But the second narration adds also something new, the detail of the rib, something taken from man's side. It may be asked whether this detail—which, as all agree, has a symbolical meaning—also refers to something strictly historical? Does it belong to that category of figurative elements which carry the thought beyond the image, and carry it not only to a disembodied fact stripped of all concrete connection with the text, but to a particular concrete, truly historical fact which corresponds to the imagery?

Caution here is of the essence. In this account the narrator moves on a plane of image; God *fashions* the dust, *breathes* his breath, *takes* a rib, *builds* on it. Since the verbs have to do with imagery, one might ask if the objects of these verbs are likewise imagery? The dust of the earth may be an image of the material element of man. Is the rib a symbol of that human nature which the woman enjoys as well as the man, but dependently upon him?

A figure of speech does not destroy the fact it describes; indeed, it may be a way of translating God's actions into human language. Of course, the sacred annalist does not describe the birth of humanity as a contemporary of Joan of Arc might relate the marvelous story of that saint. Not only is the nature of the facts opposed to this, but the character of the narrators also. An exegete who is a historian will not give the same interpretation to the account of our beginnings as to an account of the life of Joan of Arc. The exegete is more concerned with the ideas suggested by the text, revealing as they do the intention of the inspired author, than with his own personal ideas of history, and he will seek to disengage from the figurative imagery whatever facts God has deigned to make known to us, and as God has deigned to communicate **them to us,** with or without their individual characteristics.

The first account is often explained in the light of the second, being paraphrased and completed with the help of the details borrowed from the second narrative. Would it be more logical to explain the images of the second account along the line of thought followed in the first chapter?

As some of our most competent critics assure us, the *first chapter* of Genesis, despite its place at the beginning of the Book, is posterior in date to the text of the second chapter. The author of the first chapter deliberately divested his creation narrative of the traditional images which seemed to supply the narrative with historical details. His predecessor had written: "Yahweh Elohim formed man out of the dust of the earth. . . . Yahweh Elohim breathed the breath of life. . . . Yahweh Elohim made a rib of Adam into a woman"; he would say in his clear, limpid prose: "Elohim created man in his image and likeness. . . . Elohim created them male and female." The figurative description then yields to the original historical fact, abstracted from every concrete note or singularity.

May we not, in our remarks, imitate the theologian who tells the story, and like him freely interpret the images he used in his popular account?[43] The realistic description given in the second chapter urges us to probe beyond the letter. At each stage of the creation of the woman there is a corresponding picture: Yahweh

reflects and deliberates (2:18); Yahweh organizes a
parade of the animals before the man (2:19-20); Yahweh extracts a rib from the man and makes it into the
woman (2:21-22). These three scenes are connected,
the first preparing for the second, which in turn is
directed towards the third.

All exegetes agree that this divine deliberation is
a delightful touch, and that, although it is a literary
device, its purpose is to glorify the creation of woman.
As for the parade of the animals before Adam, it goes
without saying that God is not to be pictured as a
hunter. Even if everything took place with the greatest decorum, it is impossible to imagine this parade or
presentation of the animals without perceiving something ludicrous about it,[44] which is the reason why a
good number of Catholic authors look upon it as a
symbolical account.[45] The writer of the second and
popular account was giving us a lesson through the
medium of things, expressing in this concrete manner
the abstract proposition that "between man and animal there is a community of nature."

But if the first two scenes are dramatic literary
presentations, may we not say the same of the third,
which is a normal continuation of the other two? This
catechetical instruction appears to be an album whose
every page is filled with images which are both colorful and theologically true. The theological truth involved is extraordinarily profound: *the woman is a
human person and possesses the same nature as does*

the man. Previously, in order to convey the truth that one part of the man is material, earthly and "dust," the author had pictured the Lord as fashioning the human body from dust of the earth. Now he follows the same procedure, permitting us to witness the formation of the woman "from out of the man." If a moment ago we could conclude, "Truly, man is dust," we may now conclude, *"Truly the woman is man."* All exegetes have insisted on this aspect of the creation of the woman, and have noted that the biblical formula —bone of my bones and flesh of my flesh—implies at least an identity of nature.[46]

But there is more. Not only is the woman, like her husband, a human person, but with her husband she constitutes the human species, Man. Human nature is total neither in the man alone nor in the woman alone, but in them both. The theologian who wrote the first chapter of Genesis expressed this truth in "scientific" language: "Male and female he created them," which some modern authors would render as: "He created mankind masculine and feminine."

Our lesson in image form presents us with a picture in which we see God detaching some part of the masculine organism out of which he would "build up" the woman. The mutual attraction between man and woman is thus explained. The man leaves his family in order to cling to his wife (2:24) and she by nature tends to return to the man (3:16). By this twofold movement the divine plan is realized; the *husband* and

116

the *wife* form a whole (2:24), the complete man, a *moral person.* We speak today of the way the sexes "complement one another," and of man's "social nature." But the lesson of things, as taught by the Bible, is better adapted to fruitful thought than are our abstract theses.

As a human person, destined to live one and the same life with her husband, the woman is subordinated to him as his aid, his helper, his "side." She is therefore represented to us as coming from the body of the man.

It would appear that the **parallel texts**[47] do not require a realistic interpretation here, but the changes that exegesis has undergone on this subject in the past fifty years advise caution. Aside from the increasingly broader explanation of the texts which deal with the Flood, we may here single out another example that is closely related to our problem. Not so long ago it was maintained that the world had been created in *six* stages or in *six* periods, because Exodus states, "Six days shall you labor . . . but on the seventh day . . . you shall do no work on it . . . for in six days the Lord (Yahweh) made heaven and earth . . . and rested on the seventh day" (Ex 20:8-11). Few today would maintain that this clear command of Exodus obliges one to adopt the realistic interpretation of the creation of the world in "six" stages or "six" periods.

Citations from the story of the creation of man and woman, and the Old and New Testament allusions to it, have a binding force equal to the passage just cited from Exodus. Saint Paul in particular used texts in a great variety of ways and with great freedom. He knew that the Spirit of God speaks to us in the Sacred Scriptures, instructing us not only by words and deeds, but also by the very literary dress in which the facts of sacred history are presented, and at times Paul did not hesitate to base his teaching on the mere setting of the biblical narratives.[48]

Tradition has seen in Eve born of Adam a prefiguring of the Church which issued from the pierced side of the crucified Christ, and this typology holds whether it rests on a historical or a literary reality. Let us repeat that God tells us something in the Sacred Scriptures not only by what he says, but also by the way in which he expresses himself. After having developed the patristic argument and fully aware of the weakness of his own conclusion, one theologian (Père Goupil) declares: "The relation of the nascent Church to Christ being real, it is fitting that the prefiguring of Eve born of Adam be real also." "It is fitting," the author says. And rightly so. Such a proof is based on *fittingness;* but its contrary is not then necessarily unfitting.

In an allocution to the Pontifical Academy of Sciences (November 30, 1941), His Holiness Pope Pius XII did not, it would seem, intend to settle this question. He confined himself almost to the letter of Genesis: "Only from man could another man come who would call him father and progenitor. The helper given to the first man by God comes from man also, is flesh of his flesh, and was made to be his companion. Her name comes from the word man, because she was drawn from him."[49] The Pope was particularly making the point of the essential superiority of man and woman over the animals. Neither Adam nor Eve had an animal as "father and progenitor."

* * * * *

In addition to the resources of literary criticism and history, the Catholic exegete has at his disposal a higher light, the directives of the Church. Unlike the non-Catholic or modernist, a son of the Church believes that, wherever passages with a dogmatic or moral bearing upon which the Church has made some pronouncement are concerned, the true sense of the Scriptures is not the one which he may fancy that he has discovered, but the one "which holy Mother Church has held and does hold, to whom it belongs to judge what is the true sense and the interpretation of the Holy Scriptures."[50]

The Church has never made an official pronounce-on the passage in question, but some fifty years ago she did intervene in its regard through the Pontifical Biblical Commission, which returned a negative answer to the query: "whether we may call into question the literal and historical meaning of the first chapters of Genesis where there is question of facts which touch

119

upon the fundamental teachings of the Christian religion." Among these facts it singled out for particular mention the *formation of the first woman from the first man.*[51]

The Biblical Commission did not insist upon a definitive, irrevocable assent here, for its decision did not involve the Church's infallibility. The Commission is "in no way opposed to *further and truly scientific examination of these problems in accordance with the results that have been obtained during these forty years.*"[52] But so long as its decree has not been formally or equivalently modified, Catholic exegetes are obliged in conscience to recognize the interpretation sanctioned by the Commission as being "**sure**," so long as grave reasons have not been adduced to the contrary. And even then one is not to air his opinions imprudently, although he may honestly point out the difficulties which he feels modern science encounters in following what he may think to be an outmoded directive.

* * * * *

"So long as the response has not been modified." That these are not empty words is evidenced by the fact that the Holy Office in 1927 again took up a response it had published in 1897.

One might object that an explanation prohibited many years ago as a threat to the very *foundations of the Christian religion* might well be fraught with danger today also. Let us then put this document in its historical context, in order to grasp its full import.

The response of the Biblical Commission (June 30, 1909) came at a time when Catholic exegetes were dismayed and disconcerted by the bold stand taken by Loisy in his famous work on Babylonian myths and Genesis 1-3 (1901). Impressed by the recent discoveries of the Babylonian tablets and driven by apologetical needs, some of them were tending towards radical solutions which would have undermined the historical value of the first chapters of Genesis. Harried by new and bold systems which were supported by a great display of erudition, Catholic science was indecisive and lacking in self-confidence.

The theory of a materialistic evolution, on the other hand, was winning an ever greater number of supporters. The scientists had monopolized the new trend and were attacking the Church's traditional doctrines, seeking to open a breach in Christianity by exploiting and interpreting—however badly—the findings of paleontology. The statement, "Man has come from the apes," was heard everywhere. The Church reacted vivgorously. In 1895 the Holy Office condemned *L'évolution restreinte aux espèces organiques*, by Father Leroy, and in the following year the work of the American priest, Father Zahm, was, at the instance of the Holy Office, withdrawn from circulation.[54] It may be that the 1909 degree which singled out the *formation of the first woman from the first man* as among the historical facts that touch upon the very foundations of Christian religion was intended to act as a brake to slow the progress of an evolutionism which was unacceptable both because of its basic defects and because of the anti-religious use being made of it. The response, then, was part of a co-ordinated defense against even a mitigated form of evolution.

But if the first man is the result of God's touching-up an animal, why could not the first woman have come from an improvement of a female animal? Because the Biblical Commission states formally that the Woman came from the first Man. Man may perhaps have come from an animal, but not the woman. Thus, from whatever angle the question is viewed, the idea that God took an animal, then improved upon it so as to make of it a man from whom he then drew a woman, is clearly an artificial concept aimed at harmonizing two opposing points of view. *In reality it harmonizes nothing.*

Catholic partisans of evolution are then understandably embarrassed by the story of Eve's creation. But they do not despair of seeing their hopes some day realized: "Later modifications of the original idea (of transformism) by scientists . . . and also by the philosophers call for a new consideration of the problem, and herein lies the hope of many present-day theologians and scientists."[55]

Have these hopes and dream been fulfilled? An ever-growing number of exegetes and theologians, stimulated by the encyclical *Divino Afflante Spiritu* and emboldened by the liberal directives of the *Letter to Cardinal Suhard*, have worked out—the usual reservations being made—an explanation in which symbolism is given a larger place. God used Adam's body in forming Eve's. In what way? Perhaps as H Lusseau suggests, (although his view is far from certain), it was as an *exemplar-cause*, in the sense that the first woman was created or modelled after the first man. Unlike the animals, among which Adam found no helper like unto himself, Eve shared one and the same nature as Adam.[56]

❉   ❉   ❉   ❉   ❉

And now let us draw up a list of our certainties and our uncertainties. The **certainties** are:

1. The woman was formed by God and has the same nature as man.

2. According to the divine plan and in view of the propagation of the human race, she is the natural complement of man and a "fit" helper for him.

3. In the conjugal society the woman, by reason of the unity and indissolubility of marriage, is physically and morally dependent upon the man.

The **uncertainties**:

The exact manner of the formation of the woman by God.

A second uncertainty revolves around *how many* representatives of the human race there were. The second account is clearly in favor of the traditional doctrine: one primitive couple, a single man and a single woman. But let us frankly recognize that the names of our first parents are what are called collective names: man, woman; husband, wife. Moreover, the sacred author may have stylized and schematized the history of the beginnings. To show that God created mankind he pictures the Creator producing a man and a woman. The Babylonian scribes followed the same procedure in their creation accounts. The goddess Mami produced seven male forms and seven female forms; seven being the numerical symbol of totality, these seven couples symbolized the universal creation of human beings. According to the tradition preserved in the *Poem of Creation*, Marduk constructed four men. But four is one of the master-numbers of the earth, being that of the four points of the compass. By this fourfold creation, then, the earth was peopled.[57]

But did the author of Genesis really conventionalize the history of the begininngs? Did he attach all men to God by making of the man and the woman types of humanity itself? There is no question but that the history of the patriarchs contains such simplifications, but decisions on this score must wait upon further research.[58] The problem of the unity or multiplicity of the first men is a difficult one, which we must consider in detail in the following chapter.

Our remarks thus far have given no hint as to the birthplace of humanity. The sacred text provides a seemingly definite geographic clue: the woman was formed in a garden of Eden which was watered by the Tigris and Euphrates rivers, and we shall also follow this clue in the next chapter.

Weighty problems indeed, and we have merely touched the high points. And other problems, not less grave, will arise apropos of the drama which occurred in Eden.

NOTES

1 As one author writes, "The current seems to have breached the dikes. The objections of traditional theologians are finding fewer and fewer echoes" (M L Jugnet, *La Pensée Catholique*, 1949, fasc 11, 24).

2 J Guitton, *La pensée moderne et le catholicisme* (Paris, 1936), 4.

3 H Rondet, "Les origines humaines et la théologie," *Cité Nouvelle* (1943), 970.

4 P Humbert, "Enquête sur les raisons actuelles de l'incroyance," *La Vie Intellectuelle* 5 (1934), 188-189.

5 V Marcozzi, SJ, "Poligenesi ed evoluzione nelle origini del l'Uomo," *Gregorianum* 29 (1948), 343 ff.

6 Msgr Amann, "Transformisme," *D T C* 1395.

7 A M Dubarle, OP, *Les Sages d'Israel* (Paris, 1946), 19-20.

8 *De hominis opificio*, ch 5; *P G* 44:131-134.

9 The Stoics insisted strongly upon the world's subordination to man. "We well understand," wrote Lactantius, "how much truth there is in the opinion of the Stoics, who held that the world was made for us" (*De ira Dei*, 13:1). The same idea appears in Cicero: "Everything in the world was prepared and brought into being for the good of men" (*De natura deorum*, 1, 62:154). The Fathers of the Church often took up this theme: Origen, *Contra Cels*, 4, 74 (*P G* 11: 1144-1145); St Gregory of Naz, *P G* 36: 612.

10 St Gregory of Nyssa, *op cit*, ch 3; *P G* 44:133-136.

11 Cf chapter 1, note 6.

12 Origen, *In Joan*, 13, 49. Cf Is 6:8, "I heard the voice of the Lord saying: Whom shall I send and who will go before us?" Père Condamin, SJ, writes, "The idea is probably to represent God in the company of his servitors of the heavenly army, who celebrate . . . his glory (v 3) and are interested in seeing it triumph over the earth (cf I Kings 22:19; Ps 89:7)" (*Le Libre d'Isaie* [Paris, 1905], 43). Cf also Job 1:6; 2:1.

A great number of the Fathers thought that the plural, as in Gen 9:7, did not indicate a dialogue with angels, but between the divine Persons. (See the many references in Lebreton, *History of the Dogma of the Trinity*.) Moreover they have written long and profound commentaries on the notion of the "image of God." We should not forget, it is true, that the Holy Spirit who is the principal author of the Scriptures surpasses the "spirit" of his instrument; thus, the words which he inspires can sometimes have a richness and fullness of which the human author had not thought. However, any allusion to the Trinity is improbable here. If we put aside the reference to the *'elohim*, we shall see in Gen 1:26 a plural "of deliberation," or again "a plural of contagion" (J. Coppens). "In the use of the cohortative the plural is most frequent and most natural. It slipped in under the pen of the author out of habit or inadvertence, and this the more easily in Gen 1:26 because the name Elohim was itself a plural form" (*E T L* 19, [1943], 56).

13 *Advers Haeres*, 5, 6; *P G* 7:1138.

14 Père Condamin, SJ, after translating this passage from the psalm, "And thou hast placed him a little below the angels," comments on his translation as follows:

"*Angels,* (LXX, Syriac and Hebr 5:7); in Hebrew *'elohim, a god,* if you wish, but not *God.* The preceding context is violently opposed to this inasmuch as it notes the infinite distance separating God and man. This is an allusion to the sphere of spiritual and moral beings to whom man belongs according to Gen 1:27. The translation 'angels' (LXX, Targum and Rabbis) amounts to the same thing."

15 *Human Destiny,* 112 ff.

16 "A collective noun is recognized by the fact that the adjective, pronoun, verb referring to it is in the plural" (Joüon). The absence of the article in Gen 1:26 does not suggest a plurality of primitive couples. In the hexameron the divine commands ordinarily designate the projected works without the article (3, 6, 14, 24), whereas the description of the finished work ordinarily has it (6, 16, 25).

17 St Gregory of Nyssa noted this indefiniteness of phrase and used it as a basis for his distinction between *man* as pre-existing in the mind of God, *all mankind,* and *historical man* whose creation is narrated in Genesis 2. "When the Scripture says: God created man, the name given to the man created is not this or that determined name, but the name of universal Man" (*op cit,* ch 16; *P G* 44: 185-186).

18 This sentence by its rhythm calls to mind the first verse of the Babylonian *Poem of Creation,* "When on high the heaven had not been named, firm ground below had not been called by a name . . . no reed of the marshes had appeared." Cf also Prov 8:23 ff. This rhythm corresponds to the natural movement of the thought. We spontaneously make use of it when we explain creation to children. Cf below, p 255.

19 "The first author (ch 1) teaches nothing about the chronology of the works which he arranges in a simple, illuminating, logical order; nor is the second concerned with the chronological order, but refers everything to the utility and honor of man" (M-J Lagrange, OP, "L'Innocence et le Péché," *R B* 6 [1897], 371 f). Different scientific notions may have suggested a different order to the two authors. The final redactor, by juxtaposing them, showed thereby that he did not attribute a strictly objective value to the order of facts.

20 *De Genesi ad Litt,* 6:12; *P L* 34:343.

21 The conception of man as one born of the earth and of a divine element is found in the Babylonian accounts wherein the Creator kneads the clay mixed with the blood of a god. In Greek mythology, Prometheus forms man out of clay and animates him by stealing a bit of heavenly fire.

22 According to the literary critics, the section of the Bible from which these two texts are taken derives from the same source as Gen 2:7 (document J, so called because in it God is called Jahveh or Yahweh).

23 Cf De Sinéty, "Transformisme," *D A* 4, 1846.

24 F Ceuppens, "Le Polygénisme et la Bible," *Angelicum* 24 (1947), 27-29. In the same article the author asks, "Did God directly take dust for the formation of the body of the first man, or did he take the body of an animal which he had disposed to receive the human soul at the moment of the infusion of the soul?" He answers, "I think both theories can be defended, but I am inclined towards the second."

For what follows, it will be useful to consult the current literature on this problem; cf Introduction, note

3, and the following works: J Franklin Ewing, SJ, "Précis on Evolution," *Thought* 25 (1950), 53 ff; W Keller, "Humani Generis and Evolution," *H P R* 53 (1953), 620-625; Cardinal Lienart, "Science and the Bible," *Commonweal* 50 (1949), 241-243; 265-267.

25 "Polygénisme," *D T C*, 2532.

26 "The origin of the human species is thought of as of a human individual who is the result of a biological process which prepares him and of which he is the term. There is evolution in both cases, and in both cases, creation. The appearance of spirit in no wise interrupts the course of the physio-biological phenomena. We have here a supercreation, or as Leibnitz puts it, a trans-creation, but in the strictest phenomenal continuity. It is a crowning, not autogenous, but conjoined. It is a blossoming *in materia,* in the very matter itself, although it is not *vi materiae,* that is, not in virtue of the matter alone." (Sertillanges, OP, *L'Idée de Création* [Paris, 1945], 152). "Humanity begins all over again in each of us. The cycle of the pre-Adamite preparations, if it did exist, is resumed in some way by the generative cycle" (Sertillanges, *Catechisme des Incroyants* [Paris, 1930] 1, 198). Cf also E Amann, "Transformisme," *D T C*, 1365-1396; D Dubarle, "Science de la vie et dogme chrétien," *La Vie Intellectuelle* 18 (1947), 6-24; M Flick, "L'Origine del corpo del primo Uomo," *Gregorianum* 29 (1948), 397-400.

27 "L'Innocence et le Péché," *R B 6* (1897), 363.

28 *Op cit,* 40.

29 With regard to Gen 2:27, A M Dubarle, OP, (*Les Sages d'Israel*, 9) writes, "Formed from the dust of the earth,

he [man] was animated by receiving in his nostrils the divine breath which became his own breath of life. This detail, noted here exclusively for man, emphasizes the special providence exercised over this privileged creature, but not, properly speaking, the spiritual nature of the human soul, for elsewhere the Bible represents animals also as vivified by the God-given breath of life granted to them for a time." Our commentary takes these remarks into consideration, without, however, rejecting the traditional argument in favor of the spirituality of the soul.

30 It is not possible to draw any certain proof from I Cor 15:45-46 in favor of the "earthly" origin of Adam's body. St. Paul simply recalls the narrative of Genesis without wishing to settle to what extent the account should be taken in its proper sense.

31 *A A S* 8 (1941), 506-507.

32 Cf *A A S* 10 (1943), 506; English edition (N C W C) # 36.

33 *A A S* 17 (1950), 2, 575 f.

34 Cf St Thomas *I Sent*, Dist 18, q 1, 1; *Summa Theol*, 1, 92, 3; Cornelius a Lapide, *In Gen* 2:21.

35 J Coppens, *Apologétique*, 1052.

36 F Ceuppens, OP, *Genèse I-III*, 138.

37 H Junker, *op cit*, 43.

37a P Goupil, *Une Théologie en Francais, Dieu*, 2, 84-85.

38 Cited by Lagrange, OP, *art cit*.

39 The comparative meaning of the preposition, *min*, means "She is more than my bone and more than my

flesh," that is, more than those related to me by blood. Hence the reflection of 2:24.

40 Lagrange, OP, *op cit*, 348-349.

41 Is there some folklorish element underlying this parable? In the Sumerian myth, *Enki and Ninhursag*, the goddess Ninhursag gives birth to eight divinities, the seventh of which is the goddess Ninti (a name evocative of rib), who served to cure the ills from which Enki suffered. The goddess' name contains the word for rib (Ti), and by popular etymology gave rise to a myth. It is easier to ask if some such popular tale was the starting point for the historical parable in Genesis 2:21-22 than it is to answer. (Cf S N Kramer, *Enki and Ninhursag* [New Haven, 1945], 20-21, 30; Pritchard, *A N E T*, 27-41). According to Dubarle ("La Drame du Salut dans la Genèse," *La Vie Intellectuelle* 20 [June, 1949], 353), the detail of the rib may be a "happy thought suggested perhaps by the general structure of the chest and stomach, expressing in a simple and popular way the basic identity of nature between the two sexes, and the dependence (which sin would change into slavery) of the woman in relation to her husband." Cf Pritchard, *op cit*, 37, 13, 41.

42 Here and above we have referred to a "real, historical fact" in order to point out that we are not taking the word historical in the narrow sense of the past deeds of men.

43 An evolutionary doctrine which takes into account the creation of the soul by God finds no contradiction in the Bible, which teaches nothing about the "how" of the creation of the first human couple. Cf Alex Jones, *op cit*, 93.

44 Lagrange, OP, "L'Innocence et le Péché," *R B 6* (1897), 364. On this occasion he quotes the reflection of Cajetan: "Adducere animalia coram Adam et non invenire inter ea adjutorium correspondens ei, si secundum litteram intelligitur, ridiculam inquisitionem significat; in cujus mente verti poterat in dubium, an inter aves inveniretur adjutor correspondens Adae." Cf T A Collins, OP, "Card Cajetan's Fundamental Biblical Principles," *C B Q* 17 (1955), 363-378, esp 369.

45 "Some Catholic authors think that the account is a symbolic one in which the author attempts to show: 1) the superiority of man over the animals; 2) his supreme dominion over the animals; 3) the peace and happiness of paradise; 4) perhaps also the man's extraordinary knowledge" (Ceuppens, OP, *op cit*, 136). It will be noted that the peace and happiness of paradise are brought out much more vividly here than in the first chapter (cf 1:29-30).

46 Cf Gen 29:14; Judg 9:2; 2 Kings 5:1; 1 Chron 11:1; etc. Cf M J Gruenthner, SJ, *art cit*, 25, "This account of the formation of Eve may be partially figurative, . . . without professing to reproduce the facts with photographic accuracy."

47 Eg, 1 Cor 9:7-12; Ephes 5:28-30; 1 Tim 2:13-14.

48 The use he makes of Melchisedech (Hebr 7:3) is a good instance of this. Cf also Ephes 4:8.

49 *A A S* 8 (1941), 506-507.

50 *Tridentine Profession of Faith, Enchir Symbol*, 995.

51 Response of June 20, 1909, *Enchir Bibl*, 334.

52 Cf the letter of Fr Vosté to Cardinal Suhard, *H P R* 572.

53 *Enchir Symb* 2198.

54 The name Zahm no longer appears in the *Index* of forbidden books (Rome, 1946).

55 Msgr Amann, "Transformisme," *D T C,* 1393.

56 *Précis d'Histoire biblique* (Paris), 55-56.

57 Cf *A N E T,* 60 ff, 100.

58 A M Dubarle, OP, *op cit,* 20 f; J Chaine, *Le Livre de la Genèse* (Paris, 1948), 54.

CHAPTER FOUR

"And He Placed Him In the Garden of Eden"

The first two chapters of Genesis are, as it were, a prologue to human history. In them God disposes and arranges the scene (1:1-18) and introduces the actors: the man, the woman (1:26-28; 2:7, 18-25), and the animals of the fields (1:24-25; 2:19). One of the animals is to play a leading role in a spiritual drama of world importance. The first act now begins.

Up to this point Genesis has given an exclusively divine account of the works and deeds of the Creator, who is the source of harmony and beauty in the universe (1:31). Now it takes up the history of creatures. "Left in the hand of his own counsel" (Ecclus 15:14), the man will freely decide his own lot and the success or failure of the divine plan. Begun in Eden and heavy with implications of tragedy, this is a drama which will only be resolved in the heavenly paradise (Apoc 14:21-22).

The history of primordial mankind is disconcertingly *original* and surely covers tens of thousands of years. The Bible stakes out this immense period with but a few landmarks and a few brief scattered facts, such as the murder of Abel, the catastrophic deluge, the construction of the Tower of Babel, and the dispersion of peoples. In place of details, Genesis provides us with two genealogies full of barbaric names and fantastic numbers. Is it possible to reconstruct the course of a history with such meager documentation? Certainly not history in the modern sense of the word. Still, these few elements help us grasp the general direction of the religious evolution of humanity.[1]

This primitive history stands in marked contrast to other and later accounts. From Abraham on it is possible to give approximate dates to the events of the patriarchal period, and they can be fitted, it seems, into the chronology of the ancient East. The migration of Abraham, for example, coincided with political and social movements which characterised lower Mesopotamia in the second millenium as an aftermath of the Amorite invasion (1900-1700 B C). At God's call the Abrahamic clan again moved from Haran (Aram-na-harayim, "Aram of the Rivers"), being pushed westward by waves of the Hurri which broke from the north, carrying groups of shepherd people along with them in the direction of Syria and Palestine. Many details concerning these events are reflected in the lives of the patriarchs.[2] Literary critics have detected traces, in some of these accounts, of documents which link the Bible with the historical annals of Oriental peoples (Gen 14).

Nothing similar to this is to be found in the *primitive* history given in the Bible, wherein there are no dates, nor even the suggestion of what we would call a chronology. There is a superficial precision, to be sure, but it is not everywhere the same and a closer look at it serves to dissipate the illusion. Scraps of documents are indeed sometimes referred to, but they disappoint rather than reassure us, for they lead us to troubled literary sources wherein a free use is made of mythology.

It is then not possible to treat of the first and the later chapters of Genesis in exactly the same way. No modern scholar would interpret this story of the creation of the universe (Gen 1) as he would the story of the patriarchs. All recognize, in varying degree, the artificial and symbolical character of Chapter 1. Why should not the same concession be made for Chapters 2 and 3, both so similar to it in content? From another point of view, why should the history of primitive humanity be subjected to the rigorous interpretation given to the patriarchal period, when they are so different in many details?

137

"Is it possible to put the story of the origin of the world and of humanity (Gen 1:9) and the story of the patriarchs (Gen 12:1) on the same plane in the 'history of beginnings'? Is it not clear in advance that, in these two sections, the relation of the writer to his sources and, through them, to the events which he relates, is essentially different? Will not the way they express things, then, be radically modified by that fact?"[3]

But because these chapters form part of a book which has been traditionally looked upon as historical, it is to be assumed that they contain the true story, a divinely guaranteed accounts of events which once really happened. As we shall see, this assumption will be changed into certainty by an examination of the text. This history stands in a class by itself and cannot be judged in the light of Graeco-Latin or modern literary styles. It relates "in simple and figurative language, adapted to the understanding of a less developed people, the fundamental truths presupposed for the economy of salvation."[4]

I

In the first act the curtain rises on a sumptuous setting designed by God himself. *The Lord God (Yahweh Elohim) planted a garden in Eden, to the east* (2:8).

The first scene of the drama takes place in a *gan*, a garden. In the Sumerian language, a "gan" is a fertile, well-irrigated, luxuriant enclosure. This garden was situated in a fruitful region in *Eden*. "Eden" or "Edin" was the term for a rich region. Lying between the cities of Lagash and Umma, near the Persian gulf, this desirable territory was the cause of incessant rivalries. The people of Lagash held that this "Edin" was a region very dear to their god Nin-Girsu. Another "Edin" in Syria-Palestine is mentioned as being the property of the god, Amurru. What are we to conclude from these resemblances, if not that the garden in Eden by its very name evoked the idea of a privileged place, a place of pleasure, which God in his bounty had prepared for our first parents?

It would, however, be imprudent to formulate any definite geographical conclusions based on these indications.[5] The mention of "the east," which is perhaps a gloss, is too vague to be of much use to us.

* * * * *

In the Orient, fertility is largely a matter of irrigation (cf Gen 2:5; 13:10). *A river rose in Eden watering the garden, and from there it separated into four branches* (2:10). This is an odd way of putting it. We moderns say that the tributaries *flow into* the main stream; here the main stream flows into its tributaries. For us the head of a river is the place where the water rises out of the ground; in the present text the *head* corresponds to the river's junction with another stream.

Our astonishment will not be so great if we put aside our manner of thinking and adopt that of the river-people along the Euphrates and Tigris. An ancient and complicated network of canals has been discovered in lower Mesopotamia. Kings were praised in ancient writing for their irrigation projects. The Sumerians excelled in the making of canals, and in their language developed certain technical terms descriptive of that art. Each canal had three parts: the "mouth" or "head" was the point at which the canal touched the river; next, the canal itself; and finally, the "tail," which was the lake or basin wherein the waters were "bound" or held in reserve for times of dryness. According to this terminology, then, the "head" was not the *source* of the river, but the point at which the tributaries were adjudged to flow out from it.

Two of these rivers are well-known: the Tigris (Hiddeqel) which flows east of Assur, and the Euphrates. Famous throughout the Orient, these sacred rivers go back, according to tradition, to the very beginnings of the world: "Marduk created the Tigris and the Euphrates, he put them in their place, with a good name he named them."[6]

One will look in vain in any atlas for the other two rivers. The Phison "encircles the land of Evilath," where there was gold and bdellium and onyx; the

Gihon encircled the land of Cush. As a geographical item this is not very enlightening, and the exegetes have tried many times to identify these two streams. The majority opinion identifies the Phasis with Phison and the Araxes with the Gihon, because their sources are not far from those of the Tigris and Euphrates, in Armenia; but nowadays we more correctly look to the regions of lower Mesopotamia, in the neighborhood of the Persian Gulf, which in days of old was called the Salt River. Moreover, in the third and fourth millenia the Gulf of Persia extended farther inland, so that the Tigris and Euphrates, which now flow as one into it, then emptied separately into the Salt River. Other rivers of the southern basin of the Tigris and Euphrates suffered the same fate as the two larger rivers; one, Uknu (modern Kerka—Gihon), the other, the Ulai (modern Wady Karum—Phison). They flowed in an easterly direction down from the Zagros mountains, where the substratum abounds in precious minerals (gold? onyx?), and like the Tigris and Euphrates, they too once flowed into the Salt River by distinct estuaries. As the Persian Gulf receded they changed their courses, and their waters mingled with those of the Tigris and the Euphrates, of which they have become tributaries.

Let us now transport ourselves in thought to the western banks of the gulf, and look with the eyes of the ancient river-people at the spectacle which presented itself. The *River* ascends from the south (from

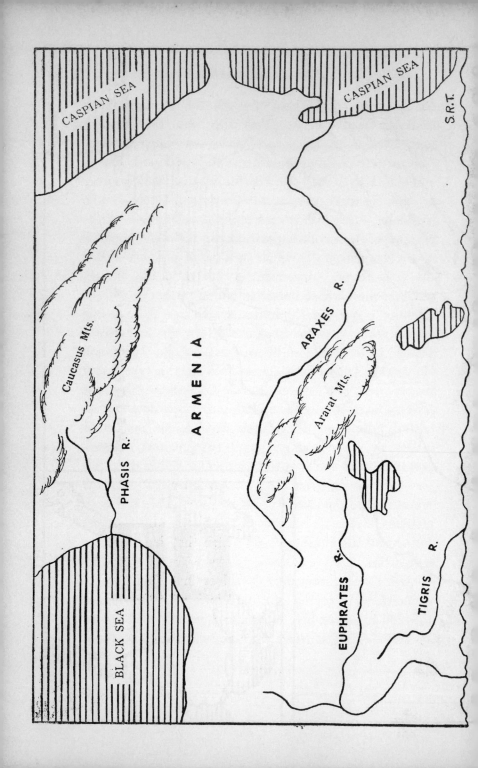

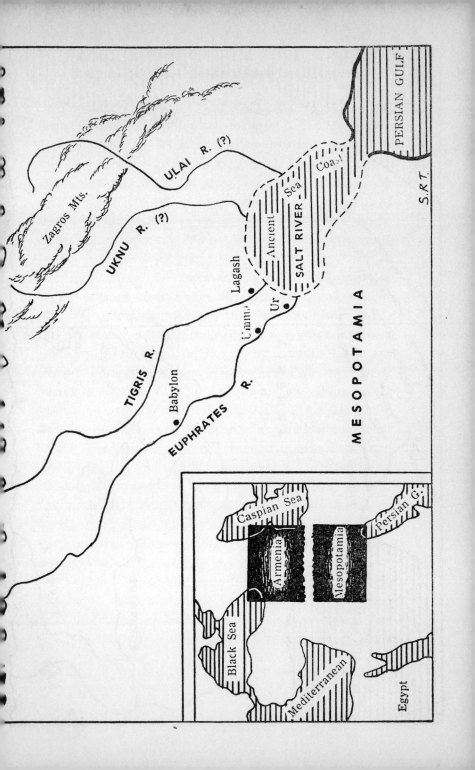

the region of Eden?) and bathes the region about. Then the "River" divides itself into four "heads," that is, it gives rise to four branches: to the east, the first "head" is the beginning of the river Ulai (=Phison?) whose "tail" loses itself somewhere in the mountains to the east; the second head corresponds to the point where the waters of the River are deflected "into" the Uknu (=Gihon?); finally, still closer to us is the head of the Tigris (the river which waters the city of Assur) and the head of the Euphrates.

The cradle of humanity, then, is to be situated in either northern or southern Mesopotamia. To the north—in Armenia—if we consider the heads of the rivers to be their sources, for the Tigris and Euphrates, the Phasis and Araxes rise in widely separated regions in the mountains of Ararat. To the south—in lower Mesopotamia—if we follow the Sumerian terminology. It is on the banks of the Salt River that an ancient popular tradition placed the marvelous oasis where grew the "tree of the gods" with its magnificent fruit, the "isle of the blessed," the blessed land of Dilmun (?).

In both hypotheses the topographical details are taken in a strictly objective way, for both consider the sacred author as describing paradise for the purpose of instructing us as to the geographical location of the garden of God. But is this true? What is the value of this supposition?

As early as the 3rd century of our era, Origen had experienced doubts on this subject, but he lost his

144

way amid subtle allegories. His bold exegesis scandalized the literal-minded interpreters of his time. Saint Epiphanius hurled this argument directly against him: "I myself have seen the waters of the Gihon; I have seen them with my own bodily eyes; they are waters like those of the Euphrates, which can be felt and drunk, and have nothing spiritual about them."[7] From then on, how could anyone question the reality of the rivers of paradise!

The topography of the Garden of Eden reveals some striking anachronisms. At the origin of humanity (at least 40,000 or 50,000 or 100,000 years ago[8]), there was surely no question either of the Tigris and the Euphrates, or of the land of Cush, or of the city of Assur. A redactor may have substituted more recent names for the archaic ones, or he may have revived and modernized an old tradition (just as one might write in "New York" on an old map of New Amsterdam).[9] But the difficulty remains. How explain the persistence of these two Mesopotamian rivers over thousands of years despite cataclysms which have radically changed the face of the earth? Then too there was the Flood, which, we hold, was a historical reality.

There is a further difficulty: why was the exact location of the primeval habitation not etched upon the memories of peoples? "Sem—who saw Lamech, who saw Adam—also saw Jacob, who saw those who saw Moses; therefore the deluge and the creation are true."[10] This argument of Pascal may have sufficed for an earlier generation and may convince those who today (erroneously) look upon the biblical genealogies as so many tight links in a chain, but his argument cannot stand up before literary and historical criticism. Humanity is much more ancient than the older exegetes thought. The sacred author arranged his genealogies in a conventional numerical framework; and even at a time when greater attention was paid to a strict chronology, St Matthew was not above using such an artificial method (Matth 1:1-17).

How then can we reasonably hold for an oral transmission, extending over thousands of years, of minute details regarding the topography, the boundaries and the hydrography of the earthly paradise? By a special act of his providence God could have insured the integral transmission of his teachings, of course. But did he do so? Was it fitting that he do so?

It is more and more widely accepted that history cannot demonstrate the existence of an oral tradition whereby the heritage of the primitive revelation has come down across the centuries. "Such a long transmission, without writing, without a spiritual magisterium, cannot be explained."[11] The impossibility of proving the fact of such a tradition, the immense space of time over which it would have had to be preserved, and especially the remark in the Bible (Jos 24:2, 14-15; Judith 5:7-9) that Abraham's forefathers were polytheists, render it likely that "there was some positive intervention on God's part, restoring to mankind the essential truths which it had forgotten, and upon which the whole of revelation was to be based."[12]

But if we have some hesitation about the oral transmission of "essential truths," there is all the more reason for questioning the preservation of secondary details. If God permitted essential truths to be forgotten and altered, was it fitting that he intervene to safeguard a tradition which provided information on topography and the course of rivers? "Can man have preserved, across thousands of years of existence, in all its primitive, unblemished and original colors, an account of the Fall which comes to us through the channel of a tradition in which there flowed nothing but pure, absolutely uncontaminated water? Neither revelation nor theology asks us to admit such a paradox."[13]

Why could God not have prompted the sacred writer to borrow the details of an ideal description from either the geography of his times, or from the traditional folklore, or even from mythology, in order to suggest to his readers the original happiness and the delights of the *garden of God*? When the prophets painted their picture of the messianic age and wrote its history by anticipation, did they not in their descriptions integrate details drawn from contemporary chronicles, from the geography of their times, from the society of their period, and from their local traditions? Examples of this abound in the writings of the prophets, who boldly projected the present into the future.[14] Anachronistic? Yes, but not error, for the prophets were conscious of the relative value of these literary devices.

Now why could not the historians of the golden age, like the prophets who announced the messianic age, have projected the present, not into the future, but into the past? To be sure, the literary forms of history and prophecy are not to be confused, but here we are dealing with two concrete situations which are undeniably similar.

Both the narrator of Genesis and the prophet of the messianic age present us with a cross-section of history. But while the one tries to resurrect the past, the other seeks to bring to life scenes of the future. Their subject eludes them both. Einstein's, "We cannot send a telegram into the past, still less into the future," fits the case perfectly. The future belongs to God and to him alone, but the Eternal One raises the prophet to himself and brings him into contact with his knowledge. The historian of the golden age was equally helpless. To make primitive humanity live again, he had no witnesses at his disposal who went back in an uninterrupted line to the very beginnings of things. God, therefore, who sees what for us no longer exists, had to intervene in order to communicate his light either to the inspired author himself, or to the immediate ancestors of Israel.

But if this be so, may not the comparison be continued? Why not apply to the descriptions of the prophet of the past the judicious remarks just made concerning the prophets who were the historians of the future? Why may we not speak of the "historical dress" of the first chapters of Genesis, that is, the inevitable tint given to the language of the narrator of Genesis by the period in which the author lived? Why not speak of the genius proper to his people, of the institutions which surrounded him, and of his own personal mental endowments? God did not insulate his chosen writers from these influences, and it is not difficult to understand the reason why. If he had revealed to the historian of the beginnings all the conditions of life of the period in which the events took place, would he not thereby have reduced the seer of the past to the role of a passive instrument, and have rendered his message not only mysterious but unintelligible to his contemporaries? Oftener than not the supernatural light which was granted to the messengers of God threw light only on the substance of things; the true and the precise manner of their fulfillment remained in the shadow as far as they were concerned. It was up to the inspired author, then, to translate the divine message without parodying it, any alteration of it on his part being excluded by the privilege of inspiration.

We believe, then, that in this work of translation the sacred writer used all the resources at his command. He described the earthly paradise according to the geography of his time, or an ideal geography whose secret is unknown to us. He makes us think of those artists who depict Gospel scenes in Florentine landscapes and who, unmindful of anachronism, clothe the Madonna in the sumptuous robes of a Roman matron.[15]

It is quite probable that the literary artifice which has been detected in many other passages has likewise been used here.[16]

＊　＊　＊　o　＊

In this ideal spot our first parents were to enjoy what was useful and pleasing to them: *the Lord God (Yahweh Elohim) made to grow out of the ground all kinds of trees pleasant to the sight and good for food* (2:9a).

In this enchanting scene two trees with mysterious names stand apart from the others: one, a tree to be avoided—"the tree of the knowledge of good and evil" —and "the tree of life." *The Lord God (Yahweh Elohim) made to grow out of the ground all kinds of trees pleasant to the sight . . . the tree of life in the midst of the garden, and the tree of knowledge of good and evil"* (2:9).[17]

Some authors would uproot **the tree of life** from the Garden of Eden as if it were foreign to the original narrative, something transplanted from another territory and clumsily re-planted in the garden of paradise. But the tree of life did not grow exclusively in the earthly paradise, for examples of it are found elsewhere. The Assyro-Babylonians knew of a "plant of

renown, thanks to which man has his breath of life."
Gilgamesh in his search for immortality had ardently
desired and vainly sought for the precious herb of life,
and sharp-eyed scholars have, they think, discovered
reproductions of a stylized tree in Sumerian drawings
of the 3rd millenium B C. Egypt also has preserved
the memory of a plant which distilled an elixir of immortality for both gods and men, a plant, it was be-
lieved, that grew to the east of heaven. Finally, according to Iranian traditions, the *Haoma* conferred
health, strength and longevity,[18] and well deserved its
name as "the plant which keeps death at a distance."

For a long time to come, men will continue to discuss the efficacy of the plant of youth or the tree of
life, and scholars will hesitate to identify the sacred
trees mentioned in Oriental literature or engraved on
stones. We are here in the presence of a theme repeated over and over again, with variations, throughout the whole of the Orient; in a word, a traditional
figure. In the land of Sumer, in Assyro-Babylonia,
Egypt and Iran, the "king of terrors" (death) obsessed
men's minds. The cruel necessity of dying clashes so
violently with that deep-rooted self-preservation which
is part of our nature that men have everywhere tried
to solve the mystery of death. Man dies because he
has lost the "tree of life," the "plant of life," the "waters
of life," the "food of life," and he dreams of recover-
ing the "plant of youth" which promises to make "young
men out of old."

Did the Bible create these images out of thin air?
Or did it import the tree of life from Babylon and
plant it in Eden?

Before answering these questions, certain things
must be explained. About 1940 or 1750 B C, Abraham,
the ancestor of the Jews, emigrated from Ur-Kashdim,
an ancient city far down the Euphrates, where Sumerian and Semitic influences fought for the ascendancy.
He took with him not only the terminology, juridical
concepts and scientific notions of his milieu, but also
a host of images and traditional ideas. The divine
call which drew him forth from polytheism did not
cancel out his secular culture. We have already seen
some traces of this ancestral terminology and of the
scientific notions of the ancient Orient,[19] and historians
usually point to parallels between the Sumero-Baby-
lonian code, the social and juridical customs of the
Hurri,[20] and those of the patriarchs.

But the Spirit of God had to cleanse the recipient
of his revelation from all such elements as were incompatible with the truth. Returning from Harran,
Jacob made an inventory of the sacred objects in his
family for the purpose of getting rid of the idols (Gen
35:2-4). Abraham, when turning to the one God, had
performed a like purification, purging the religious traditions he had received as a legacy from ancestors who
had served other gods (Jos 24:2, 14-15; Judith 5:7-9).
With the help of a light from on high he integrated
the elements of his culture into a new vision of the

152

world. Elements thus incorporated into the new synthesis thereafter assumed a new value, serving as the expression of that revelation of which Abraham was, by divine favor, to be the depository,[21] and this transposition was the model for many other sublimations which later religious history was to witness.

There is no doubt that the theme of the tree of life formed a part of the Assyro-Babylonian folklore. The sacred author may have taken it over, transformed it and given it a higher meaning, but the religious tradition or new synthesis into which he worked the theme of the tree of life *differs essentially* from mythological accounts. Although the problem of death torments men everywhere, the solution given in the Bible is radically different from the explanations of death given in the *Myth of Adapa* or the *Poem of Gilgamesh,* as most critics concede and our commentary will prove.[22]

The mention of the tree of life completes the ideal description of the Garden of Eden. In the mind of the author, paradise was not only the place where our first parents were to live in happiness, it was also the region of life; to live there was the same as to escape death. By his very constitution man carries death within himself, for he is dust. By way of privilege, however, he was able not to die; he had the power and the grace to be immortal, although the future realization of that power was contingent upon a condition never to be fulfilled. In fact, this privilege

153

would remain an ideal promise—a lesson in things which from the start set forth an ideal which was actually to be realized in eternity, when sin and earthly infirmity would be no more.

Theologians and exegetes sometimes ask if it was enough for the man to eat once and for all of the tree of life to be made immune from death. Would he not rather have had to eat of that marvelous fruit from time to time, in order to repair the wear and tear on his organism? How did the tree guarantee the human body against dissolution—by the very nature of its fruit, or by a supernatural force communicated to the life-giving tree by God?[23]

These questions are all pointless if the tree of life was only a *symbol of a bodily immortality* which was promised conditionally to our first parents (cf Apoc 2:7, 22:19). As long as the man and the woman remained in the earthly paradise, here pictured as the region of life, they would not die; but the very moment they withdrew from it they would be exposed to death.

* * * * *

The second tree, that of the knowledge of good and evil, arouses our curiosity. This time the neighboring literatures furnish us with but feeble light, at least in our present state of knowledge. Historians usually point to the "tree of truth" mentioned in the Sumerian inscriptions of Gudea, to the "talking-trees" of Dodona, and to the "laurel tree of Delos" with its prophetic rustling, but these are far-fetched comparisons.

The tree in question is placed in the center of the garden where it is clearly visible.[24] This prominent position emphasizes its exceptional importance. The narrative, in fact, revolves around the tree: *Of the fruit of the tree in the middle of the garden God (Elohim) said, 'You shall not eat of it'* (3:3). But this localization, however much it brings the tree out into bold relief, does not thereby reveal its nature.

A tree is proverbially known by its fruit; so let us try to identify the fruit of this mysterious tree. The woman seems to be well-informed about it, for after mentioning the first prohibition of the Creator she continued to quote him: *You shall not touch it, lest you die* (3:3).

Actually, there is something of feminine exaggeration about the woman's statement. But we should not in turn exaggerate, for the woman was merely repeating, but with a slight change, the threat uttered by God himself. The Lord had said, *But from the tree of the knowledge of good and evil you must not eat; for the day you eat of it, you must die* (2:17). It would be blasphemous to attribute a meaningless threat or a pedagogical lie to the Creator. Despite the naiveté displayed by our ancient author's use of images, he had a very exalted idea of God.

Was the tree, perchance, poisonous, producing a deadly fruit? Some have held this view, but wrongly.

Our first parents were not poisoned by their *act*. Death was the penalty for their *disobedience*, but it was not the tree itself which by an immediate and natural consequence brought death to them.

To complete our inquiry, let us have words with the serpent—without, however, imitating our mother, who was too gullible! *The serpent said to the woman: 'No, you shall not die, for God knows that when you eat of it, your eyes will be opened and you will be like gods (Elohim), knowing good and evil'* (3:4-5).

In one particular the serpent contradicts the Creator who had couched his threat in categorical terms saying, "You will surely die"; the serpent now maintains the very opposite, "You shall not die." The liar! (Cf John 8:44.) But intermingled with the lie, the words of the serpent contain a grain of truth; he interprets the name of the tree in his own way: once man's eyes are opened, he will *know good and evil;* and, wicked exegete that he is, he concluded with the false statement, "You will be like God (Elohim)."

What is this *knowledge of good and evil* that is connected with the fruit of the forbidden tree? The first tree bore the name "tree of life" because it was related to the privilege of bodily immortality enjoyed by our first parents. The second tree probably deserved its name because of its relation to the knowledge of good and evil. What was this knowledge?

According to some, "to know good and evil" means "to grasp, to distinguish good from evil." Before eating the fruit the man and woman supposedly knew nothing of this distinction, being like children who had not yet attained the age of reason (Deut 1:39; II Sam 19:36 [?]; Is 7:15-16), and it was the tree that occasioned the awakening of their conscience. Some few texts of the Fathers, carried farther than the texts warrant, are adduced in support of this position. According to Clement of Alexandria, "the first man, fully enjoying paradise, was still God's *little child*. When he succumbed to voluptuousness (symbolized by the serpent which crawls on his belly, an earthly vice, a turning towards matter) he allowed himself to be seduced by his desires. Become man in his disobedience and having been disobedient to his Father, God, the child was ashamed before him."[25]

Before the temptation, Clement maintains, Adam was as ignorant of sex as a child. But was he also ignorant of the distinction between good and evil? On this point the Alexandrian says nothing.

Theophilus of Antioch writes: "Adam, as yet only a child in years, could not properly receive knowledge. In our day, a new-born child cannot yet eat bread, but is fed first with milk, and then, as he grows older, with solid food. Thus it was with Adam. . . . God wished the man to prolong his state of simplicity and integrity by remaining a child. It is of divine and human law that one be subject to his parents. . . . Moreover, it is not normal that small children have thoughts beyond their years."[26]

157

Saint Irenaeus, evidently depending on Theophilus of Antioch, goes on in the same vein: "The beings that were to serve man had already reached their full growth while the master was yet a small child who, naturally, had to grow in order to attain his perfection. . . . The man was a child, he had not the perfect use of his faculties, and as a result was easily deceived by the tempter."[27]

But does the relative ignorance of the child necessarily imply his lack of moral discernment? And were our first parents children? Of course—in the sense that they both enjoyed an integral and innocent nature, but they were also "children" who had reached the age of reason.

Not that we must adopt the medieval explanations of the extraordinary knowledge possessed by the first man. The Council of Trent had worked out a decree which stated, using the words of the Scriptures (Ecclus 17:6), that the gifts of science and wisdom had been given to Adam. But the point did not even come up for discussion, and modern theologians rightly imitate this reserve. Genesis itself suggests that cultural development began *after* the Fall, and was a gradual process. Little by little man mastered and exploited the world, thus fulfilling the program given him by the Creator to "fill the earth and subdue it."

From the first, however, man was endowed with intelligence and a sense of morality. He perceived the nature of animals (2:20a), understood his own superiority over them (2:20b), and the purpose of the woman and her providential role (2:23-24), thus indicating a knowledge far beyond the capacity of a small child. A denial that our first parents could tell the difference between good and evil runs counter to the spirit of the narrative. "If the man and the woman had acted in complete innocence, like animals which graze on a neighbor's lawn or in their master's vegetable garden, we could understand how Yahweh might have expelled them from the garden in order to prevent them from trespassing again (3:22); but we could not then explain the severe penalties he inflicted upon them."[28]

Such heavy penalties were not a punishment for childish behavior, but imply a serious culpability, a responsibility, and consequently a knowledge of good and evil on their part. We read in Ecclesiasticus, in a passage filled with allusions to Genesis: "He gave them counsel, and a tongue, and eyes, and ears, and a heart to devise; he filled them with the knowledge of understanding . . . and showed them both good and evil."[29]

Other exegetes, following Theophilus of Antioch, held that God had forbidden our first parents to aspire to a knowledge beyond their intellectual capacity, as, for example, the knowledge whereby one sees the profound reason for the distinction between good and evil, between the goodness or evil of things. By yielding to their *excessive* desire for knowledge, they say, Adam and Eve tried to arrogate to themselves a superhuman prerogative and to enter into rivalry with the supreme legislator. Their sin, then, was an intellectual one!

This interpretation squares well with several details of the account. The "knowledge of good and evil" likens one to the *Elohim:* "When you eat of it (the fruit) . . . you will be like God (the *Elohim*), knowing good and evil" (3:5). After the Fall Yahweh ironically declares, in the presence of the "god" who failed, "Indeed, the man has become like one of us, knowing good and evil" (3:22)![30] Moreover, this explanation is a faithful reflection of the habitual cast of Hebrew thought, so often hostile to human wisdom and anti-intellectual.

But does it harmonize all the nuances of our account? We think that it does not.

It has been noticed that in the Bible contraries are often opposed so as to convey the idea of a totality. Examples are not lacking in Genesis.[31] To know good and evil, then, meant to know *everything*. Thus, the tree of the knowledge of good and evil was the tree which led to one's "knowing everything."[32]

On the other hand, after their fault, the knowledge acquired by our first parents calls for something experimental, and of the moral order: *The eyes of both were opened and they realized that they were naked* (3:7). This knowledge goes beyond a purely theoretical knowledge; it is above all an "experience," and what a painful experience! The man and the woman now

160

feel within their own bodies an inward lack of balance
and the baneful effects of their disobedience. This sen-
sation troubled them and aroused complex feelings in
them of which they had hitherto been ignorant, such
as shame, fear, distrust, the impression of being contemptible. They now flee from God's sight: *I was
afraid because I was naked, and I hid* (3:10).

Such was the knowledge gained by the first man
(3:11); it involved an experience, and the moral order.[33]
To know good and evil, then, would be to allow oneself *every kind of experience*. There is no question,
then, of "either a knowledge of discrimination or an
exhaustive knowledge, but of a knowledge of good and
evil. . . . It was a knowledge in which the good and
the evil were mingled, a combined, associated, mixed,
a cumulative knowledge of good and evil . . . the
knowledge of sin."[34] Our first parents, led astray and
blinded by the serpent's words, aspired to this knowledge which shimmered before their eyes. Their temptation resembles strongly the temptations which present day novelists, modern tempters that they are,
stir up in the hearts of our youth: "To act without
asking whether one's action is good or bad. To love
without worrying whether it is good or evil." André
Gide's hero, led on by such deceits, would sample
all earthly fare: "I wish . . . to eat of all fruits
which the branches stretch out to me. . . . I put my
hand boldly upon all things, feeling that I have rights
over all that I desire." Much bolder was he than

161

Balaam, who confessed himself powerless to do anything of his own accord, whether good or evil (Num 24:13). This claim of a right to experience all pleasure without being subject to a higher rule implies that man arrogates complete moral autonomy to himself.

Was this knowledge supra-human, divine? Yes, for the lying serpent attributes to God and to the mysterious beings who dwell in the court of Yahweh a privilege which many peoples falsely attributed to their divinities, namely, that of not being held to the moral laws made for human beings alone. Satan is very clever at equivocation, and each of his words can be interpreted in different ways. "To know" may be to understand or to test, or both together; "good and evil" stands not only for the whole of moral values, but also everything that is good and bad, pleasing and displeasing, useful and harmful; "to be like Elohim" means to resemble both God and the other heavenly beings. Equivocation thrives under the artful touch of the tempter. God "knows good and evil" because he is the supreme rule of morality—but how false to suggest that the Lord acts well or evilly, according to his whim! The angels of God judge good and evil (II Sam 14:17); but they are not exempt from the rules of goodness.

By forbidding the use of the fruit of the tree of knowledge of good and evil, God forbade the man to "try everything once," and obliged him to exercise his freedom only within the limits of the divine law. But our first parents would overreach themselves; they would commit a sin of pride.

In what concrete manner did they abuse their free will and revolt against the will of Elohim? Many would reply at once: "By eating an apple!" But this popular opinion has no scriptural foundation whatsoever. Others with as little proof think that they ate from a fig tree instead (cf Gen 3:7). Still others, and they are in the majority, recognize the mystery, say that it was a fruit, and let it go at that.

A few modern exegetes, impressed by the progress of symbolical theories, have essayed a few careful steps along the path of symbolism. The precept, they say, perhaps did not bear on the fruit of a tree, but envisaged a kind of restriction regarding food. It consisted in a command regarding food which imposed upon the pride always possible for a richly favored nature a definite acknowledgement of dependence, to be proven by their voluntary abstinence from food.[35] To preserve the underlying historical sense of the narrative, it is said, the thing forbidden must be considered in the same area as the symbol. Since on the symbolical plane there is question of a fruit, food must be involved on the plane of the historical reality.

This is not impossible, for Noe, the second father of the human race, was to receive a command regarding abstinence from food (Gen 9:4). But a symbolical setting would still serve to bring out historical fact even if the forbidden object did not fit into the category of food. Moreover, the main proposition itself is an unprovable hypothesis. How often in the study of the biblical symbols and parables have we not noticed that the lesson or thing signified is very loosely illustrated by the symbol or parable! It is certainly not possible to lay down as a principle that the thing symbolized must be looked for in the same sphere as the symbol itself. Let us then simply admit that the sin of pride has been portrayed for us in a form which we do not understand.[36]

Finally, mention may be made of an explanation which periodically finds champions in certain intellectual circles. In very elevated terms, and with the best of intentions, M Guitton has recently proposed it as a "probability" based upon a "guess."

"Some exegetes have held and hold that in Oriental symbolism (a trace of which is found in the Canticle of Canticles), the tree of knowledge of good and evil . . . represents the feminine nature, inasmuch as it can be for man the cause of a moral fall; for the false love, false attachments, the deceptive pleasures of knowledge and false foods of this earth which divert man from his spiritual goal spring from woman.

"We are led to think that Yahweh imposed a temporary trial upon our first parents, which consisted in their maintaining a complete reserve between them until such time as God had determined. As the man and woman were, doubtlessly, a very young couple, the wisdom back of the divine command can be readily understood.

"The ancient author thus gives his readers to understand how highly God values mastery over oneself and the reserve often called for within the sphere of what is licit; and how valuable that chastity is, which, even in marriage, preserves the spirit and the fire of virginal love, which preserves also the essence of conjugal love, guards it against routine and fatigue, sanctifies and renews it, and causes it to be born over and over again. In our days, when so many thinkers have taken up again this crucial problem of Christian morals, it should be pointed out that the difficulty existed from the beginning of our race, and that it perhaps constituted the trial of that single society from which the human race has issued.

"This leads us to conclude that humanity has not appreciably changed, and that the same problems and the same solutions remain from age to age, as do the same sufferings of the Christian, the same happiness, the same Via Crucis."[37]

Some of the ancient commentators—Saint Clement of Alexandria, Saint Zeno of Verona, and undoubtedly Saint Ambrose—looked favorably upon this view;[38] Saint Augustine knew of it, but mentioned it only to reject it with a blunt *"Ridiculum illud est*—How ridiculous!"[39]

The proponents of this theory, however, base their stand on several details in the account. Here are some of them.

It was Eve who inveigled the man to do evil, the woman who was the cause of the temptation. Does not this circumstance indicate that the woman herself was the object and the instrument of the sin?

It was the tempter's use of an equivocal word, which meant both intellectual knowledge and conjugal relations, that led to the act of disobedience. The verb "to know" is a euphemism for the marital act. Is it not also a discreet allusion to the nature of the first sin?

It was, finally, on the occasion of their disobedience that Adam and Eve became conscious of their nakedness. Does this coincidence not allow us to suspect that there was a close connection between sex and the sin?

All very weak, indeed. It is true that through the centuries woman has very often used her charms so as to become an instrument of sin, but she has absolutely no way of making a man break the law of God. Besides, in the present case there is nothing to indicate that the divine precept consisted in the provisional prohibition of the use of marriage. The text, on the contrary, insists strongly and realistically on the woman's role: she was created to complete the man in view of the propagation of the species (2:24).

The tempter's formula was equivocal—granted! The experience tasted by our first parents did not measure up to their hopes. They had counted on the divine privilege of being able to try everything; instead, they now experience, much to their unhappiness, a disorder in their nature. The disturbance they now feel does not prove that their sin was one of the flesh. It was their disobedience that upset the balance of their nature, and the disorder reverberated in their bodies. Before their sin our first parents knew sex without being embarrassed by it; after it they knew the disorder of sex and felt shame. The sacred author drew attention to this result at once, not necessarily in order to teach us the nature of the transgression, but because *the unruliness of the senses was the first external sign of the Fall,* and he thus resolved a problem which so engrossed the Sumerians and the Semites.

This theory finds little support in tradition, and owes its new vogue to the publication of certain Assyro-Babylonian texts. Undoubtedly it would be a gross exaggeration to pretend that the tree of knowledge was in the ancient Orient a symbol for feminine nature,[40] but we might be able to discover, in the *Epic of Gilgamesh*—although it takes good eyes to do so!— a hint that sense-pleasure contributed to an advance in intelligence.

The *Epic of Gilgamesh* relates the astonishing adventure of Enkidu, a strange creature who had been kneaded from clay by the goddess Aruru. At first he lived in a state of savagery in the steppes, "knowing neither people nor land." He was covered with hair like a wild beast and shared the life and food of animals: "He ate grass like the gazelles, to drink he bent over like the animals." He defended his companions, the wild beasts, from the snares of the hunter, filling the pits with dirt and stealing the nets of the enemy. To get rid of Enkidu, the hunter planned to lure the savage to the city. A harlot would seduce him. The uncivilized, innocent man of the forest allowed himself to be duped, and as a result Enkidu could "no longer live with the wild beasts and the gazelles"; his heart was no longer satisfied with herbs and water, his nakedness made him unfitted for human society. Enkidu left the steppes and went to dwell in the "country." His whole personality changed. "Thou are become like a god," the harlot assured him.

In all this description, one verse of the poem has attracted much attention: "And he (Enkidu) now has wisdom, broader understanding." As the seduction produced its effect, Enkidu noticed the development of his mind and his conscience, as if the excitation of his senses had opened his mind.

Now, it would be dishonest not to admit that there are *some* similarities between Genesis and the story of Enkidu in the *Epic of Gilgamesh*. Adam and Enkidu were both victims of a woman and both, before their temptation, had lived happily in the company of animals. The tempter of Genesis promised his victims that they would be "like gods"; the temptress of the *Epic of Gilgamesh* flattered Enkidu and, in order to lure him into a civilized land, compared him to a god, "Thou art become like a god." As the result of his sinful actions Enkidu acquired a higher culture: he became "civilized." Adam and Eve, after their sin, "knew" their nakedness.

But it would be equally dishonest to pass over in silence *the essential differences* between the two accounts. In the Babylonian poem nothing is said of the origin of humanity; Enkidu is not the first man! Enkidu gambols joyously on the steppes in the midst of gazelles; but the company of animals does not satisfy Adam, who desires a helper like himself. Enkidu, as a consequence of his relations with the harlot, finds his way to civilization, and in exchange for the company of animals becomes the friend of Gilgamesh, a great hero. In a word, Enkidu definitely comes out ahead, whereas Adam forfeits his privileges and is the loser. And finally, it is impossible to liken Eve to the harlot of Uruk.

Even granting—a hypothesis we are not prepared to concede—that some details may have been borrowed from old Assyro-Babylonian traditions and incorporated into the descriptions of Genesis, it is clear that they have been infused with an entirely different spirit.

Professor Coppens has recently proposed an original variation of this interpretation. He thinks it proable that the hagiographer was combatting the Canaanite cult of the fertility gods and goddesses. The serpent symbolized these vegetation gods. "By presenting Eve as talking to the serpent, he depicts her as forgetting her Creator and as being tempted to put herself and her husband (Gen. 2:6), and consequently their marital life, under the aegis, protection and blessing of licentious pagan cults." Eve's temptation, then, consisted in "believing that she could obtain the supreme blessing of being able to transmit life, not from Yahweh, but from his principal adversaries, the false gods who, at the time when the account was put into writing, were considered the gods of vegetation and fecundity." The sin of pride committed by our first parent was, then, accompanied by a transgression against the sanctity and consecration of marriage. When later on Eve became a mother, she would confess her henceforth unshakeable faith in the creative power of Yahweh, and would repudiate forever the temptation to which she had momentarily yielded.[41] *"I have given birth to a man-child with the help of the Lord (Yahweh)"* (Gen 4:1).

❖   ❖   ❖   ❖   ❖

Our exposition has shown the direction being taken by contemporary exegesis. An increasingly greater importance is being given to the scenario and to the literary form of the drama. At the end of the 19th century, the biblical accounts were as a general rule

taken literally pretty much as they stood, and along
the lines of the commentaries of preceding generations.
The integral "historical character" of the first chapters
of Genesis was strenuously defended. Thus with the
exceptions of a few anthropomorphisms which were
not taken literally, the biblical account was understood
to relate the story of the beginnings as it had really
taken place, and Genesis 2-3 as the equivalent of an
eye-witness account. Today, however, "the question
of the historical reality of the material circumstances
of Genesis 2-3 has generally come to be looked upon
as an open question. The Church has not thought it
necessary to exercise her authority here, a fact that
would be quite incomprehensible if her important
teachings were being threatened, especially since a
considerable number of modern exegetes have aban-
doned the interpretation which was formerly almost
a common view."[42]

But does not history then go up in smoke? By no
means! We should bear in mind that the literary forms
of Gen 2-3 "correspond to none of our classical categories and cannot be judged in the light of the Graeco-
Latin or modern literary styles. One can therefore
neither deny nor affirm their historicity taken as a
whole, without unduly attributing to them the canons
of a literary style within which it is impossible to clas-
sify them."[43]

So-called traditional exegesis has tended to affirm
en bloc the strictly objective value of all of the details

171

of the description of paradise. Rationalistic exegesis denies the historical value of the biblical accounts, and ranges the Bible with mythological legends. Modern Catholic exegesis endeavors to distinguish, insofar as it can with the help of comparative methods, between the historical reality and its external garb. Exegetes, as a rule, do not hold that the sacred author composed his history as a dramatic and picturesque exposition of philosophical ideas, theological concepts, moral conclusions; they do, however, think that he related historical events of a religious nature using a setting whose elements were borrowed from his secular culture, from folklore, from the traditions of Assyro-Babylonian mythology. A description containing imagery may very well be the vehicle of authentic history. The Biblical Commission does not oppose such exegesis; in demanding of the Catholic interpreter that he maintain the "historical literal sense," the Commission avoids the expression *"proper* literal sense," as it wishes to leave the exegetes free to have recourse to symbols, provided that they definitely establish that through them the sacred author wished to express historical facts. Exegetes will, of course, differ as to the extent to which the imagery overflows into the history. Is it enough to retain only a broad and general objective connection between the figurative scenes and the historical reality so described? Or should certain details be given a value surpassing the image and representing the real? Each case must be examined by itself, as it is impossible to make any *a priori* pronouncement according to our present ideas of history.

The historical realities, or as Father Vosté has said, "the fundamental truths presupposed for the economy of salvation," are these:

By the divine favor our first parents were created in a state of perfect happiness. They lived in a state of grace. All this is signified by the garden of pleasure, by the well-irrigated and fertile enclosure.

According to the divine intention and by way of privilege, it was possible for our first parents not to die. This is signified by the "tree of life" in the middle of the garden.

They enjoyed, moreover, an internal equilibrium, and although naked, felt no shame. According to Saint Thomas, this immunity from concupiscence was due to original justice and a perfect harmony of nature, because the body was subjected to the soul, the sensible faculties to the mind and will, and these to God, a kind of pre-established harmony, as it were. . . This subjection was easier then than it generally is now in the state of sin, abstracting from the beneficent influences exerted by the Redemption. It is also certain that the *fomes* (the "fuel" of sin), that spontaneous irritability of the sensual appetites, was not radically extinguished, but only restricted in its exercise.

This perfect happiness, with the twofold privilege of corporeal immortality and immunity from death, was connected with the sojourn in paradise and familiarity with God. The sojourn itself was conditional upon obedience to the divine precept symbolized by the "tree of knowledge."

This historico-idealistic interpretation avoids two perils here, one of "reduction," the other of "separation." The first danger lies in wait for those who seek unity at any price. In other fields, they reduce life to the physico-chemical elements of matter, make man similar to an animal, and faith to a psychological mechanism. Following the lead of Loisy, they trace biblical traditions back to mythological legends, and revelation to the material elements it uses. They make the hagiographer a writer of myths, and, in short, deny the *transcendence* of revelation.

The second danger awaits exegetes and theologians who are insufficiently aware of the "literary, scientific, historical, cultural and religious problems connected with these chapters," of the "literary processes of the early Oriental peoples, their psychology, their way of expressing themselves and their very notion of historical truth."[44] There is thus the danger of isolating and separating the sacred author from the environment in which he lived, from the civilization which nurtured him, and from the contemporaries for whom he had to frame his message. This is to run the risk of forgetting that revelation is, as it were, *incarnate* in the human mind.

174

II

But now a new actor, the serpent, enters upon the scene. In the drama about to unfold he will play the role of protagonist analogous to that of the traitor in classical tragedy.

This actor is not lacking in intelligence; he is familiar with the precept of Yahweh-Elohim (3:1), he reasons and argues cleverly, ably presents his case against God (3:5), seduces. Moreover, he does not restrict his role to the drama of paradise, but roams about on a worldwide scene. Throughout the ages he has been the foe of humanity. Against him the children of Eve will struggle. But a day is to come when he will suffer a complete defeat. This actor, who perdures from generation to generation, is not only an intelligent, but also a spiritual, being. He is the spirit who "always denies," the eternal enemy of the human race, "that great dragon, the ancient serpent, he who is called the devil and Satan" (Apoc 12:9; Wisd 2:24). This intelligent, spiritual, evil being receives an astonishing name, *the Serpent*.

Could it be that the narrator ascribes intelligence to a physical serpent? Hardly this, for he places the animals, the serpent among them, under the dominion of the man (2:19-20). Man alone possesses intelligence and will, and none of the animals is like him (2:20). In the mind of the author, therefore, the physical serpent should not be taken to be an intelligent being.

The problem, then, remains unanswered; why did the ancient writer so clearly identify the devil with the serpent?

Not long ago many exegetes thought that the devil, the power of evil, dwelt in the reptile and made use of it as an instrument, or least that he borrowed a reptilian form in which to manifest himself.

But again, why should the evil spirit have made use of a serpent or a reptilian form rather than of some other animal? The serpent, it may be replied, was thought to be "more cunning than any beast of the field," Gen 3:1 being adduced as proof. But where did the serpent gain such a reputation for wisdom and gile? The adequate explanation of this lies perhaps in the ideas and popular imagery of the ancient Orient.

The Sumerians, the Assyrians, the Babylonians and the Canaaneans had a tradition about serpents. In Syro-Palestine the serpent was the emblem or attribute of certain gods or goddesses of vegetation and of fertility, and its cult was often accompanied by licentious practices. Several divinities of the Babylonian pantheon were presented in the form of a serpent: Ningizzida, the "serpent god, lord of the earth"; Kadi, the "resplendent serpent god, lord of life"; and Ea, the god of the netherworld, who was sometimes represented with the head of a reptile.[45] Much archaeological evidence in the form of cylinders, seals, boundary stones, etc, testifies to the symbolical value of the serpent.[46] The cautious attitude of the ancient Semites in the presence of this mysterious being becomes understandable if they thought that it housed a spirit. We can also understand why faithful Yahwists saw in the serpent, so often associated with magic and divination, an excellent symbol or figure of the enemy of God and the seducer of man. As Chaine says, "The account obviously represents a reaction against the cult of the serpent, which the Semites often considered a beneficent power."

Did Satan make use of a real serpent in the earthly paradise, or did he only assume the appearance of one? A realistic interpretation defends both opinions, while in the historico-idealistic view the reptile is a symbolical representation of the fallen angel. To avoid any misapprehension here, let it be clearly understood that **the power which seduces is not a fiction, nor is it a pure symbol, but a reality.** What is symbol and fiction, however, is the mask behind which the reality is hidden, a traditional mask borrowed from the folklore of the ancient Orient. The historico-idealistic explanation, defended in years past by Lagrange and Van Hoonacker, is now finding a more favorable acceptance among modern exegetes.[47]

Gen 3:1 is ordinarily raised in objection against this view. *Now the serpent was more cunning than any beast . . . which the Lord God had made.* From this remark some absolute literalists concluded that

177

a real serpent was possessed by the devil. Others used the same text to prove the reality of a reptilian form. Let us simply say that the devil was well-designated by this animal which was thought to be more "intelligent" than the others.

"The sacred author was probably inspired by popular belief and pagan usages to make the serpent, the 'most cunning of animals' (Gen 3:1), the mask of a spiritual power inimical to God, which seduced our first parents. It is not impossible that he made a more direct use of a tradition foreign to Israel wherein the serpent played a similar role, but of this we have no solid proof."[48]

Let us note further that the text does not say, "The serpent was more cunning than the other animals." Might it not be properly interpreted thus: "The serpent (that is, the devil) was more cunning than all the animals of creation?" He has shown that he was more cunning than the man![49]

* * * * *

The story of the temptation is well known, and we shall confine ourselves here to a few observations.

Anyone who has attentively considered the scene of the temptation has been struck by its artistry. The dialogue is handled in a masterly fashion, and the principals are so well presented that they become universal types. With fine psychology the author follows the progress of the temptation in the heart of the woman. His naiveté is blended with great depth. "Goethe in the first *Faust*, Kierkegaard in his youthful effort entitled the *Dairy of a Tempter*, Balzac in his *Lily*, Fromentin in *Dominique*, Bourget in his *The Disciple*, and Gide in his *Pastoral Symphony*, have all brought to light, under different aspects, the mechanics of temptation in seduction. Goethe and Kierkegaard and Gide had centuries of analysis behind them."[50] But the author of Genesis was a true pioneer; with no example before him he attained the perfect work with his initial effort.

The symbolical character of the account of the Fall has made a deep impression on some interpreters, and they are inclined to look upon this scene as nothing more than a projection into the past of the common experience of humanity, or merely a dramatic portrayal of the condition in which Adam's children now find themselves. They feel that the author may have wished to conventionalize man's development at a decisive period in his life, as for example the passage from infancy to maturity, or the crisis of puberty. The carefree infant enjoys happiness and innocence, he is unaware of shame, he is not frightened by the prospect of death. But now a desire for knowledge arises in him; the tree of knowledge bends towards him branches heavily laden with appetizing fruits. Then his eyes are opened, and man becomes conscious of his unhappy condition. Yesterday, play; today, work! Yesterday the enjoyment of life without sorrow; today the thought of proximate death poisoning his existence! Yesterday his senses were at peace; today he knows internal struggle! After tasting of the tree of knowledge, the son of man becomes aware of the tragic side of life. Thus interpreted, these pages of Genesis might well deserve a good place in an anthology of existentialist literature![51]

When describing the crisis which arose in the life of the first couple, and their tragic choice, the sacred writer put his personal observations to good use, and revealed himself as a man of penetrating insight. But we would misinterpret him if we were to conclude that his *only* intention was to project the happenings of daily life back to the beginnings of the human story, and in so doing to credit the first man with the experiences of mankind, to make Adam the average man with all his physical and moral aches and pains.

It may be that the sacred author did project the painful story of daily life back to the beginnings, but at the same time he proposed to *explain* the unhappy lot of human beings.[52]

Conscious now of the disorder within him, the man avoids looking at himself, feeling himself to be contemptible—an indication of his *moral* fall (3:7). Being ashamed of himself, he feels ill at ease in God's presence—a sign of his *religious* downfall (3:8-10). He has to toil for his food, work for his living, and struggle against a hostile and accursed earth, and this reflects a *breakdown in the harmony of the cosmos* (3:17-

19). Finally, after a laborious life, the man was to *dissolve into dust* (3:19).

The special trials awaiting the woman were the pains of pregnancy and the sufferings of childbirth. She who was destined to aid and complete her husband was to be subjected in conjugal intimacy to the physical and often brutal domination of the man. She was to work out, in suffering, her vocation as wife and mother. Her maternity, the blessing of Yahweh (1:28), was to be accompanied by distress (3:16).

Finally, humanity was to fight a dangerous battle against the Dragon, an enemy who never lays down his arms (3:15).

Our narrator, with an originality which clearly marks him apart from the Babylonian poets, associated this unhappy condition with a sin which was freely and deliberately committed and with an act of disobedience prompted by the spirit of evil. The hagiographer, of course, does not use the *word* sin,[53] but he describes it with a wealth of detail: God promulgated a precept and threatened its infraction with punishment. The tempter hinted at disobedience, and offered the woman a chance to weigh the pros and cons of it. The fault was committed with full knowledge, and the guilty ones then felt the evil consequences of their act. "Nothing that can constitute, accompany, or follow sin is lacking."[54]

By the free initiative of the creature (the Serpent; and man) evil made its violent way into a world upon which the Creator had originally left the impress of goodness (1:31). Only in the "garden" of Eden was there good unalloyed with evil; after that, on "earth," men will eat a wormy fruit in which good and evil were mixed.[55] Although created to know only the good, men were unfortunately to experience good and evil. The Bible proceeds to describe the unfolding of wickedness. But there would come a day when, through the merciful intervention of the God-man, justice would superabound where sin had once abounded.

*   *   *   *   *

Perhaps we can now answer a question which up to this point we have left unanswered. It has been remarked that the first chapter of Genesis does not settle the problem of the unicity or the multiplicity of the primordial couple, and that the detailed account of the creation of the man and the woman given in Chapter 2 does not permit the formulation of a definitive answer to the question. Does the account of the Fall (Chap 3) remove all obscurity? In order to explain the universal fall from grace does the sacred author attribute that disastrous sin to the father of the human race? Was it the fault of a single person? In other words, does the Bible teach **monogenism**?[56]

There are the best of reasons for thinking that it does, as we shall see. And yet there are many difficulties in the text, many possible interpretations of obscurities, and the opposing theory of polygenism is widely debated among scientists and exegetes—even among Catholics. So important is the issue, in fact, so central to Catholic teaching, that Rome has felt obliged to speak with disfavor on the theory of polygenism.*

It will be useful, then—indeed, necessary—to consider this problem in some detail.

Our author undoubtedly shared the scientific opinions of his contemporaries, and his message is refracted through them—which does not oblige us to accept his theory of special creation, nor his geocentric ideas, nor his theories about light and the heavenly ocean. He was not interested in passing judgment on these views, and did not commit himself; the authority of God is therefore not engaged in the matter.

Can monogenism be considered (1) only as a current *opinion* of the times (like other pseudo-scientific notions), universally admitted, a part of the cultural patrimony of the sacred author. And if so, (2) can one hold that the hagiographer made use of this traditional view only as a vehicle for a divinely inspired teaching, without thereby canonizing the prevalent opinion? The teaching itself can be summed up in a sentence: primitive happiness was lost to man as a result of a historical fault. And the narrator may have

---

*Cf *infra*, pp. 192 ff.

expressed this truth by attributing the sin to a first human couple: being a child of his own times, he may have written the history of these begininngs in the traditional perspective, just as he had related the birth of the universe according to the creationistic and geocentric ideas then common. *If this* **double** *hypothesis can be verified,* one could hold that monogenism, a current historico-scientific notion, was not formally asserted by the sacred author.

"It seems certain," Guitton writes, "that the biblical author, like most of the philosophical and religious thinkers before the 20th century who took up the question of human origins, whether they were pagans or Jews, Christians or non-Christians, did not raise the question of the unity or the plurality of the primitive couples. He held for one couple as did those around him, as we ourselves would undoubtedly have done, had not paleontology and prehistoric anthropology raised serious doubts about the matter in our minds. We have therefore to determine whether this concept of unity at our origin is essential to his thesis, whether it forms an integral part of his religious teaching, or whether it was merely one of those statements to which the author of Genesis gave acceptance, as other learned people of his times did. He saw no reason for opposing it, but he would have been ready to abandon it, if shown by positive arguments that it was erroneous; the force of his thought, the very heart of his doctrine and the substance of his message, was not essentially linked up with it. At the present time it is very difficult, if not impossible, to give an answer to this question."[57]

Let us concede that the people of the ancient Orient were not overly concerned with the problem of the unity or plurality of primitive couples. But how then can one verify the first hypthosis suggested? How can one maintain *categorically* that they taught the unity of the first couple, when the Sumerian and Akkadian documents available to us express themselves so vaguely? These texts tell us of the creation of *man*, of *humanity*, of the *seed of humanity*, of *men*, of *peoples*, of the *blackheads* (that is, of human beings), and without distinction of sex.[58] In the present state of our research it is impossible to prove that monogenism belonged in the category of ordinarily accepted truths.

These ancient texts seem to suggest a plurality of couples. According to the seventh tablet of the Babylonian poem of creation Marduk created four human beings: "He whose creation was four black-headed ones" (7:113). After the deluge the goddess Mami reconstructed male and female humanity by dividing clay into fourteen parts, of which seven were to become men and seven women: "Fourteen pieces she pinched off; seven pieces she placed to the right, seven pieces she placed to the left. . . . Seven (mothers) brought forth males, seven brought forth women." The symbolism of numbers seems to play an important part in these two texts; the number four symbolizes the four major regions of the universe, while seven suggests totality.

The author of Genesis, then, shows his originality in that he portrays the human stock as consisting of a single couple. But might this not also have been a *literary stylization?* "In Genesis a whole people is frequently made to descend from a single ancestor (Amon, Moab, Edom, even Israel), and certain characteristics of the people thought to have come from him are attributed to the ancestor. Complex ethnic realities are stylized. Might not the same procedure have been used with regard to the whole human race?"[59]

The most notable case, Dubarle remarks, occurs in the history of Esau and Jacob. The relations between the two brothers prefigure and inaugurate the rivalry which will set Idumean against Jew. The Lord himself revealed to Rebecca the meaning of the conflict which separated the brothers:

> "Two nations are in your womb,
> Two peoples shall stem from your body:
> One people shall be stronger than the other,
> And the elder shall serve the younger" (Gen 25:23).

The names (Israel and Edom) and racial characteristics and vicissitudes of the two nations are expressed and in a certain measure explained by the names, temperaments, struggles of the two eponyms: the father of the race, one single man, recapitulates in his person the tribe which is thought to have issued from him.

The similarities between this account and that of the Fall are immediately evident. A same name designates the ancestor and his descendants; in the one case, two peoples bear the names of the two estranged brothers, Israel and Edom, Jacob and Esau; in the other, "men" come from the man. In both cases the destiny of the progeny is experienced in anticipation by the progenitor. Jacob, the peaceful one, opposes and finally supplants the bold, fiery Esau. Jacob, a type of the nation which is "tranquil, living under the tent," stands contrasted with Esau, a people "living by the sword"; in the course of their history, the Jews were often to defeat the Idumeans. And in the other case, the painful and toilsome life of the sons of man is, as it were, gathered up and lived in advance by Adam.

But these undeniable similarities do not cancel out the fundamental differences. The struggle of the twins in the womb of their mother, the contention between Jacob and Esau, the superiority of the younger over the elder, are events full of prophetic meaning. Were they, however, the *reason* for the relationship between the Israelites and the Idumeans? Strictly speaking, an author could, by using an artifice rather common in genealogies, attribute to the eponymous ancestor something done by his descendants. "It is difficult to determine to what extent the history of the two peoples influenced the history of their ancestors." In contrast,

187

the story of the Fall clearly suggests that Adam's disobedience had real repercussions in the lives of all
men.[60] The historian of old did not intend only to
prefigure or to describe ahead of time the destiny of
human beings, but he did expressly intend to assign
the **cause** of the universal Fall. He was not content
to teach us the moral lesson that man's disobedience
inevitably causes him misery; he declares that the
actual condition of humanity was brought about *by a
sin.* So universal a Fall is *most obviously and naturally explained* by the fault of the ancestor.

Should this sinful ancestor be identified with the
father of the whole human race? Some will urge that
in Hebrew the word *Adam* signifies simply man. In
Gen 2-3 it is a common noun, and as such, has the
definite article. In Gen 3:22 *Adam* designates both the
man and the woman. The Greek Septuagint and Jewish tradition may have turned this common noun into
a proper name and thus have heightened the impression that Gen 2-3 refer to a concrete person. Examples
are not wanting in the Bible and in history of this
sort of switch-over: the "adversary" of the older texts
(Job 1:6; Mach 2:1-2) becomes "Satan" in the first book
of Chronicles (21:1) and in the same way "Qoheleth"
("the preacher" in Ecclesiastes) has been transformed
into a proper name by the familiar usage of modern
exegetes.

But is it so certain that in these chapters the word
Adam is only a generic term? We read, for example,

that "the man and his wife were both naked, but they felt no shame" (2:25). Does this sentence not prove that at least here the common noun is applied to a definitely determined individual, to one of the "two"? *Ha'adam* would not here designate man in general, but in a precise way, the human being of the male sex.[61]

An examination of the genealogies, and in particular of the Table of Nations (Gen 10), raises a more serious problem. Many Catholic authors rightly hold that in the genealogical list of Genesis 10 there are links with no natural connection between them.[62] Some of the names in it do not refer to individuals but to ethnic groups. What is more, different races are joined together in a common ancestor: Elam and Assur descend from Sem (22), Chanaan and Egypt are from the same father (6); the Cretans are linked with the Egyptians (14), and the Hittites go back to Canaan (15). The author has substituted relationships of proximity, culture, trade, or political alliance for relationship of blood. This fact is absolutely certain and inevitably raises an important question: May not the author of Genesis have conceived the genealogy of the human race as he did the genealogies of the tribes and races mentioned in his text, grouping all men under a single ancestor, the man? Why might he not have exercised the same freedom to achieve his purpose of showing mankind to be one great family, whose members all share in the same fundamental destiny?

189

Whether all races of the earth descend from the same father or not, they form a *moral* unity: they are directed by the providence of one and the same God, and all of them have suffered a hereditary fall. No one of them, therefore, could boast of any basic superiority whereby it could claim for itself alone the privilege of dominating the earth, and of considering other human races as servants or even slaves. In such a hypothesis, the sacred author might affirm the moral unity of humanity, but not necessarily the strict unity of the human stock.[63]

This argument, since it is based on an analogy, cannot terminate in certitude, nor does it seriously challenge the traditional exegesis. However, it is enough to make a broader interpretation *possible,* **on condition that it is not excluded on other grounds.**[64]

But is not this very possibility decisively ruled out by Saint Paul (Rom 5:12-21)? So the great majority of theologians and exegetes used to hold, but for some years a new interpretation has been gaining ground. As all agree, the Apostle was not formally explaining the text of Genesis. From numerous allusions or reminiscences scattered throughout his letters,[65] we can see that he loved to nourish his theological meditations on the first chapters of the Bible; he excelled in bringing out their moral and religious lessons. In Rom 5:12-21 the account of the temptation underlies his reasoning. Saint Paul was interested less in teaching us about the origin of the human race or furnishing us with a complete explanation of the appearance of sin in the world than he was in extolling the limitless power of redemptive grace. To realize his purpose he seized upon a comparison suggested by the happenings in the earthly paradise, and drew a parallel between *Adam*, the unique source of sin and death, and *Christ*, the unique source of justification and life; between the multitude's *solidarity in sin* with their ancestor, Adam, and the *solidarity in grace* with the unique Jesus Christ of those who have been redeemed. Saint Paul's manner of speaking reveals his monogenistic point of view. Like all Jews, he adapted himself to the idea immediately and obviously suggested by the sacred account. But the question is: did Saint Paul here intend to affirm his conviction?

Not all elements of the comparison, of course, constitute formal assertions which would involve the divine authority. Thus, when Saint Paul used the name of Adam (5:14), he certainly did not intend to affirm that Adam was actually the name of the first man, any more than he wished to determine the real names of Pharoah's magicians, the enemies of Moses, when writing his second letter to Timothy (3:8). He simply expressed himself in the manner customary to his day and age.

It may further be conceded, at least in principle, that a comparison can be made even if the term which serves as its starting point has no real existence. The moral lesson drawn from the patience of Job in the

191

epistle of Saint James (5:11) does not depend on the historicity of Job. Real or fictitious, Jonas' being swallowed by the fish and his deliverance retain their value as figures of the burial and resurrection of the Lord (Matt 12:29-42).[66]

Again, Saint Paul sometimes argues from the silence of the Scriptures, or from a literary setting, without being too concerned about the underlying historical reality. The Scriptures, for example, say nothing about the father or mother or genealogy of Melchisedech. That fact alone justifies his using the priest-king of Salem as a figure of Christ and as a term of comparison, and the parallelism holds good whether Melchisedech enjoyed an hereditary priesthood or not.

Applying these remarks to the text of the Epistle to Romans, some exegetes hold that a law of interdependence and solidarity governs the spiritual condition of humanity. Just as all have been constituted sinners by a fault for which they are not personally responsible, so they are all constituted just by the obedience of another, and not by their own personal merits. In both cases, the effects of the action of an individual extend to the multitude. But the Pauline parallel, taken as a whole, shows that there is not an absolute parity between the two members of the comparison; Christ is infinitely superior to Adam. For Paul, Adam is not as fully the head and representative of humanity as is Christ. Now the Apostle had no rea-

son to abandon the unique genealogical document of
Genesis, and he had good reasons for retaining it. But
in Rom 5 his intention and attention are not focused
on this strict unity of origin. Whatever his personal
(and unexpressed) conviction may have been on this
point, it is not guaranteed by biblical inerrancy.

In this question, the best argument is Catholic tradition. The **Teaching Authority** of the Church has not
as yet solemnly declared monogenism to be a defined
doctrine; but in setting forth the dogma of original sin
it always presupposes monogenism and it always refers to the text of Romans. Thus according to the
Council of Trent, Adam was *a* man, "the *first* man,"
primum hominem, hence a concrete and individual
person. This first man committed *a* sin, *"peccatum
quod origine unum est."* This unique fault injured not
only its author, *"non sibi soli,"* but it was transmitted
by way of generation to the posterity of the first man,
that is, to the *whole human race, "omne genus human-
um"* (Sess 5:1,2, 3.).[67]

Was then monogenism (implicitly) defined, or was
it indirectly affected by the definition of the Council?

Theologians almost unanimously hold for the second alternative, and the encyclical *Humani Generis*
approves their stand.[68] Original sin is, in effect, as
"the sources of revealed truth teach (Rom 5:12-19) and
the documents of the Teaching Authority of the Church
propose (Conc Trid, Sess 5, Can 1-4)" a sin "which

proceeds from a sin actually committed by an individual Adam and which through generation is passed on to all and is in everyone as his own."[68a]

His Holiness Pius XII in his encyclical *Summi Pontificatus* spoke out against the error of racism, forcefully expounding the law of human solidarity and charity which unites all people. He remarks on the insight of the Apostle (Acts 17:26, 27), "which makes us see the human race in the unity of one common origin in God . . .; in the unity of nature . . .; in the unity of the immediate end and mission in the world; in the unity of dwelling place, the earth . . .; in the unity of the supernatural end . . .; in the unity of means to secure that end."[69] In line with the traditional teaching, then, the Sovereign Pontiff recalls our unity of physical origin, but it is permsisible to believe that he did not intend to settle the debate between monogenism and polygenism.[70]

By way of disproving the polygenist theory, it will be enough to draw attention to the insurmountable difficulties which are encountered in the attempts to explain original sin from this point of view. Either the first men came into being in a single place, or they appeared in diverse regions separated from one another. In the first hypothesis we may conclude that *all* the first men were elevated to a state of original justice, that they were *all* subjected to a trial, that they *all* succumbed before they had begotten any children, and that the whole of humanity is descended from these men. One would thus safeguard the doctrine of the universal Fall as proclaimed by the Council of Trent, but one would not then do justice to the same Council's statement that the sin of the human stock was a single sin.

To avoid this difficulty, the hypothesis of a collective Fall has been evolved. The first men were, we are assured, simple, naive, and able to be taken in by a strong personality. But one among them, either by trickery or by violence, induced the others to join him in revolt, thus drawing divine punishment down upon the race.[71] In this way a unity of sorts is maintained; the original transgressions would have been many, but they would have been made one through the initiative of the one leader. But then, how can one conceive that a multitude, which in the hypothesis was endowed with original justice and sanctity, could be tricked into sin on so large a scale? On the other hand, a collective sin supposes diverse degrees of culpability. The full freedom of the original fault would be difficult to conceive if it had to be explained by the unanimous cooperation of a multitude.

The question becomes complicated if the human groups appeared successively at varying intervals, instead of simultaneously. It would then be impossible to postulate a single leader of the conspiracy, for the "conspirators" would be spread out over different periods. These collective revolts would then have to be many, and the unity of the initial fault would be still further minimized. There would no longer be question of a sin at the origin of the human race, but of a fault at the starting point of each branch of the stock.

The same difficulties, only on a vaster scale and of much greater complexity, are encountered if these waves of humanity rose up at different epochs and in different regions of the globe.

The polygenist hypothesis, however, need not be linked with a *collective fault*, and some authors explain the universal diffusion of sin through heredity. In the beginning, they say, the various branches of human beings all benefited by that spiritual state which the Council of Trent has defined as the possession of holiness and justice. In each of these branches, at one moment or another, sin made its appearance. The supposition is not at all absurd, nor is it opposed to the doctrine of free will, for spiritual creatures are fallible. A great number of them, then, committed serious sin. Considering the immense generations separating us from the origins of our race, it is extremely unlikely that all should have persevered. These faults freely committed interrupted the transmission of sanctity and of original justice, so that each man, by tracing back his ancestry, can arrive at a first sinner who by his own free act had fallen from a better condition.[72]

This hypothesis can scarcely be reconciled with the clear declarations of the Council of Trent, according to which the *whole human race* was infected by the

sin of the father of race. In the hypothesis, a number
of men, perhaps even a great many of them, avoided
the Fall. They, therefore, were exempt from concupiscence and immortal. . . . A strange hypothesis indeed!
Would it not tempt us to minimize or even to suppress the preternatural gifts?[73]

Let us conclude, then, with the words of *Humani
Generis:* **"The faithful cannot embrace that opinion
which maintains either that after Adam there existed
on this earth true men who did not take their origin
through natural generation from him as from the first
parent of all, or that Adam represents a certain number of first parents. Now it is in no way apparent how
such an opinion can be reconciled with that which the
sources of revealed truth and the documents of the
Teaching Authority of the Church propose with regard
to original sin, which proceeds from a sin actually committed by an individual Adam and which through generation is passed on to all and is in everyone as his
own."**

NOTES

1 Cf A M Dubarle, OP, "Le drame du salut dans la Genèse," *La Vie Intellectuelle* 48 (1949), 547-559.

2 R De Vaux, OP, "Les patriarchs hébreux et les decouvertes modernes," *R B* 53 (1946), 321-348; 55 (1948), 321-347; 56 (1949), 5-36.

3 J Lévie, SJ, "L'Encyclique sur les études bibliques," *N R T* 69 (1946), 786.

4 *H P R, art cit,* 573.

5 Some exegetes look for Eden in the region of Bit-Adini (cf Is 37:12; Ezech 27:23; Amos 1:5), situated in upper Mesopotamia between the Euphrates and the Balikh. In his satire on the king of Tyre, Ezechiel associates Eden with the "hill of God" (28:13, 14, 16). Where was this hill? "In the recesses of the north" (according to Is 14:13).

6 P Dhorme, *Choix de textes religieux Assyro-Babyloniens* (Paris, 1907), 87.

7 Letter of St Epiphanius, bishop of Salamis, to John, bishop of Jerusalem; *P L* 22:522.

8 Abbe H Breuil recently wrote of 600,000 years; cf *Anthropos* 37-40 (1942-1945), 667-688. Cf E Arbez, SS, *art cit, A E R* 123 (1950), 204 f.

9 It would be interesting to study the history of the Tigris and Euphrates in Assyro-Babylonian literature. It could perhaps be proved that the Tigris and Euphrates figured in a mythological geography long before their names were used to designate the two Mesopotamian rivers.

10 Pascal, *Pensées,* # 624.

11 J Chaine, *Le Livre de la Genèse* (Paris, 1947), 7.

12 R De Vaux, OP, "La Religion de l'Ancien Testament," *Initiation Biblique* (Paris, 1939), 670. The positive intervention of God may be conceived very broadly. We need not suppose that the truths fell ready-made from heaven in a single moment, in a massive and instantaneous manner, like the fall of a monolith. The special action of God does not exclude the reflection and elaboration of the human mind.

13 J Coppens, *La Connaissance du bien et du mal et le péché du Paradis* (Louvain, 1948), 20.

14 Cf Ez 31:8-9; 48:5 ff; Apoc 22:2.

15 This kind of projection of the present into the past is verified elsewhere: "The civilization presupposed in the history of Cain and Abel, as also in Chapter 2, is that of the neolithic age, whereas man is of the paleolithic and so is much older. The whole section anterior to Abraham, therefore, is written according to a mentality posterior to the events described (J M Vosté, OP, *Angelicum* 28 [1948], 162).

16 Some exegetes would have it that the sacred author, wishing to idealize the site of paradise, deliberately brought together four famous rivers—as if we today were to picture a land which contained the Seine, the Danube, the Ganges and the Mississippi. By this procedure the sacred author would be hinting at the artificial character of his writing.

17 Concerning the two trees of paradise, cf J Coppens, *op cit,* 49 ff; *E T L* 23 (1947), 66-70.

18 In Greek mythology the gods of Olympus quenched their thirst with the immortal ambrosia.

19 Cf *supra*, Chap 2, *passim*.

20 G Ricciotti, *History of Israel* (Bruce, 1955), I, # 246 ff; R De Vaux, "Les patriarches hébreux," *R B* 56 (1949), 17-30.

21 Not that there was a *literal* borrowing in the strict sense. In the present state of our knowledge it is impossible to draw up a parallel between Gen 2-3 and the Assyro-Babylonian accounts in such a way as to determine which elements were borrowed and incorported into the biblical account. A kind of literary osmosis might well explain everything.

22 Criticis have noted several anomalies in the biblical text which point to a profane source. The tree of life is introduced by a badly constructed, "limping" sentence (2:9b); it reappears at the end in a text that is apparently a doublet (cf 3:22, 24; 23). In any case, despite these redactional imperfections the tree of life plays an essential part in the story; it is impossible to tear it out by the roots.

23 On the immortality of our first parents, see W Goosens, "Immortalité corporelle," *V D B S*, 299-313.

24 The biblical phrase, "in the middle (or midst) of," does not necessarily designate the geometric center of the garden, but has ordinarily a very loose sense.

25 Clement of Alexandria, *Protreptikos*, 11; *P G* 8:228.

26 Theophilus of Antioch, *Ad Autolycum*, Bk II, 25; *P G* 6:1092.

27 Cf *Adv haer*, 4, 28; *P G* 7:1105.

28 J Coppens, *Apologétique*, 1061.

29 Ecclus 17:5-6; compare Ecclus 17:1, 3,4 with Gen 2:7, 3:19, 1:26, 1:28.

30 Coppens has recently advanced a new translation of Gen 3:22: "Behold, Adam (man), like everyone who (or whoever) is born of him, will have to undergo (to know—in the sense of to test or try) good and evil." Cf *La Connaisance. . . .*, 118-120. On this reading of F Assensio, "De persona Adae et de peccato originali originante," *Gregorianum* 29 (1948), 505 ff; J Coppens, *E T L* 24 (1948), 414-429; R De Vaux, OP, *R B* 56 (149), 302 f.

31 E g, Gen 24:50, 31:24.

32 P Humbert, *Etudes sur le Récit du Paradis et la Chute dans la Genèse* (Neuchatel, 1940), 82-116; C Lambert, "L'expression de la totalité par l'opposition des contraires," *Vivre et Penser* (= *R B*) 52 (1945), 90-103.

33 This meaning is wholly in conformity with the Hebrew word "to know," a nuance which did not escape Saint Gregory of Nyssa. "The word 'knowledge' does not everywhere seem to designate understanding and pure knowledge, but rather an internal disposition with regard to what is pleasing" (*De hominis opificio*, 20; *P G* 44:197).

34 J Coppens, *op cit*, 17.

35 H Lusseau, *De la mesure en exégèse*, 36.

36 According to one author, Adam's sin was a sin of magic.

37 *La Pensée moderne et le Catholicisme*, fasc 9 (Aix-en-Provence, 1947), 102-103.

38 *De Fuga* 3 (*P L* 14:571); *Epist* 45:10, 17 (*P L* 16:1143, 1145); *Epist* 63:14 (*P L* 16:1193); *Expos S Luc* 7:142-143 (*P L* 15:1737). In the interpretation of these texts, it will be recalled how easily Saint Ambrose could turn from the literal sense and dwell on its moral applications. As much can be said for the medieval Doctors. In support of the sexual interpretation, Coppens cites, in addition to Clement of Alexandria and St Gregory of Nyssa, St Maximus the Confessor, St Epiphanius, St John Damascene (*E T L, art cit*, 402-408). Several of the texts can be disputed. On the thought of St Gregory of Nyssa, cf J Laplace's introduction to the French translation of *De homo op* (*La Création de l'Homme,* Sources chrétiennes), 54 ff. An examination of these texts appears in F Assensio, "Tradición sobre un peccado sexual en el Paradiso?" *Biblica* 31 (1949), 490-520; 32 (1950), 35-62, 362-390.

39 *De Genesi ad litt,* Bk XI, 41:57; *P L* 34:452.

40 What extraordinary eyesight it would take to discover this symbolism in Cant 2:3!

41 *Op cit,* 25, 26, 45.

42 Y Laurent, "Le caractère historique de Gen 2:3," in "L'exégèse française au tournant du XIXme siècle," *E T L* 23 (fasc 1-2), 54-55, 64-65.

43 Cf "Letter to Cardinal Suhard," *loc cit,* 573.

44 J M Vosté, OP, "Letter to Cardinal Suhard," *ibid.*

45 Cf Deimel, SJ, "De Serpentibus in Religione Babyloniorum," *Verbum Domini* 4 (1924), 342-344.

46 Cf Coppens, *La Connaissance. . . .,* 99-117, 123-134; Chaine, *op cit,* 49, note 40.

47 Dennefeld, Junker, Rigaux, Ceuppens, Coppens, Dubarle, etc.

48 R De Vaux, OP, *R B* 56 (1949), 307.

49 Coppens proposes this translation: "The serpent was the most naked of all the animals of the steppes."

50 J Guitton, *Le Développement des idées dans l'A T*, 115.

51 By reason of its universal, "typical" character, the crisis in the garden of Eden might serve to illustrate the crises of humanity. Cf Ezech 28:1-19; Rom 7:7-13.

52 For the penalties inflicted on the man and the woman, see Coppens, *E T L* 13 (1937), 632-640; 17 (1941), 73-75.

53 The word "sin" will appear for the first time in 4:7, in a context somewhat similar to the account of the Fall. It will be noticed that in the story of the temptation the forbidden fruit was offered with the maximum of enticement: "the tree was good for food, pleasing to the eyes, and desirable for the knowledge it would give" (3:6). Here in synthesis is all the attraction of sin. Is the tree a conventional image?

54 Dubarle, OP, *Les Sages d'Israel*, 13.

55 St Gregory of Nyssa, *De hom op*, 13; *P G* 44: 165 ff.

56 We use the term "monogenism" in the strict sense of *one single* couple at the origin of the human species. Scientists often make use of this word to express a *unity of stock*, whether this stock be made up of one or of many couples. In a general way anthropologists admit a plurality of ethnic groups, which they divide into genera or species (e g, Sinanthropus, Paleanthropus, Modern Man); these genera form diverse races (e g, Modern Man is made up of Nordics, Denarics,

Mediterraneans, Mongols, etc). Most anthropologists trace the different ethnic groups to a single stock, and from this point of view they may be called 'monogenists.' At present, however, neither paleontology nor biology allows them to pronounce for or against a strict monogenism. Will the natural sciences some day reach a final solution here? We cannot say. A noted specialist, Boule, thinks that "the origin of man is a problem which only paleontology can be expected to answer" (*Les hommes fossiles*[3], 535). Will the scientists snatch the secrets from "records taken from rocks?" One may doubt it. But is the method which depends upon fossils the only method? No one can foresee what the positive science of tomorrow may bring forth. Comte thought it fantastic to inquire about the chemical constitution of the stars, but only ten years later the spectroscope made possible what he had declared to be impossible. Prudence therefore counsels us to refrain from any *a priori* decisions in the matter. Meanwhile, we know for certain that no true scientific discovery will ever really jeopardize a truth of faith. (See once again the works cited in the Introduction, note 3).

57 *Le Développement*. . . ., 127.

58 J Plessis writes ("Babylone et la Bible," *V D B S*, 730), "The complaint is sometimes made that the Assyro-Babylonian documents are silent on the creation of the first man. It is probable that this silence will always remain—or rather, it must be recognized that the Babylonian tradition knew only of the creation of men." Cf M-J Lagrange, OP, *Etudes sur les religions sémitiques* (Paris, 1903), 339 f.

59 Chaine, *op cit*, 54.

60 Cf Gen 9:25-27, where we see a curse visited upon an ethnic group as the result of the fault of an ancestor. Compare Ex 20:5.

61 The absence of the article in Gen 3:17, 21 does not permit us to conclude that *Adam* is treated as a proper name. Some scholars think the omission is an anomaly, imputable to a later transcription. In Gen 3:22 and 24, *ha'adam* apparently has a particular meaning, that of a collectivity (?). Lefévre argues from this to the distinction of documents (*R S R* 29 [1949], 466) and Coppens finds in it some support for his new translation of Gen 3:22 (*La Connaissance. . . .*, 122, note 1).

62 Cf Heinisch, *Das Buch Genesis* (Bonn, 1930), 83, 195; Junker, *Die Biblische Urgeschichte. . . .*, 25-28; Bea, SJ, *De Pentateucho* (Rome, 1933), 183; Chaine, *Genèse,* 152-159.

63 According to Dubarle, OP *(Les Sages d'Israel,* 22), "It may be that the author of Genesis did not intend to affirm expressly the phyletic unity of the human species." Chaine (*op cit,* 54 f), for his part, writes, "Genesis by itself does not permit us to give an answer to the question of monogenism; this answer comes from the magisterium of the Church." Cf M J Gruenthaner, SJ, *art cit,* 26 f.

64 In his broad outline of biblical history, the author of the book of Wisdom devotes a few verses to the first man. He refers to the text of Genesis, but without explaining it, merely stating that the man was "created alone" (10:1). We are not to consider these words as proving monogenism, but as an allusion to a circumstance of Adam's creation: Adam was the

first one to be formed, and he received a fit helper only later on.

65 Rom 7:11, 8:20, 16:20; I Cor 6:16, 11:7-9, 14:34, 15:21-24, 45-47; II Cor 11:3; Eph 5:28-33; Col 3:10; II Thess 3:10; I Tim 2:13-14.

66 Cf A Feuillet, "Jonas," *V D B S,* 1116 f.

67 *Concilii Tridentini Acta* (Fribourg-in-B, 1911), V^2, 162-209; 233-241.

68 Many references will be found in the article of Lennerz, "Quid thelogo dicendum de polygenismo?" *Gregorianum* 29 (1948), 425-427. Cf R Garrigou-Lagrange, "Le Monogénisme n'est-il nullement révélé, pas même implicitement?" *Doctor Communis* (1948), 19 ff; M Flick, "Il Poligenismo e il Peccato originale," *Gregorianum* 28 (1947), 555-563; *Humani Generis,* # 37; *Summi Pontificatus* (N C W C), 17 ff.

68a *Humani Genesis* (N C W C), # 37.

69 *Summi Pontificatus,* Oct 20, 1939 (N C W C), 17.

70 The Holy Father quotes the statement of Saint Paul in his discourse at the Areopagus, "From one man God has made . . . the whole human race to live upon the face of the earth" (Acts 17:26). Some have thought that this does not refer to Adam but to Noe (cf Gen 9:19 and 10:1-32). According to others, Saint Luke inserted this sentence of Saint Paul's discourse into the account without guaranteeing its exactness (cf Acts 7:16). The Apostles, of course, had the gift of infallibility in their preaching when they dealt with matters of faith and morals, and if Saint Paul affirms man's descent from Adam as a doctrine pertaining to faith, then it is a part of the deposit of faith.

71 Cf "Polygénisme," *D T C*, 2536, where the hypothesis is proposed in the form of a question.

72 Cf the suggestions of Dubarle, OP, *op cit*, 21, note. He bases these notions on two texts of Saint Thomas, *De Malo*, q 5, a 2; *II Sent*, d 33, q 1, a 1, ad 3.

73 The conditional immortality of the first man was defined by the Council of Carthage (418) and by the Council of Trent. Trent teaches, in addition, that concupiscence is an "effect of sin" (*Denz* 789, 101, 792).

CHAPTER FIVE

"I Will Put Enmity . . . ."

The drama of Eden reached its climax in a banishment. Yahweh expelled the man from the garden, and at the eastern entrance to the enclosure posted the Cherubim, whose name and function call to mind those stone colossi which guarded the palace-doors in Babylon. On the path which led to the tree of life he placed a "bolt of lightning" to bar the way, a flaming, revolving sword corresponding to the metal bolts of thunder which, among the Assyrians, were the symbol for anathema and interdict.[1] The scene clearly indicates that from then on paradise was closed to the man and his descendants. Once driven from the garden whence he had derived his privileges, Adam found himself condemned to live on an earth that had been cursed. The man returned to the earth, and he turned again into earth. He began to retrogress, to return to his beginnings. After creating man God had graciously transferred him from the earth and had "placed him in the garden of Eden" (2:15). Now, in his justice, Yahweh Elohim put man *out of the garden of Eden, to till the ground from which he was taken* (3:23). As long as he remained near the tree of life, Adam had by a special privilege escaped the forces of dissolution which he bore within himself by reason of his physical constitution; subject now to disintegration, he was to return to dust (3:19). How he had changed! The change of his place of residence reflects his altered status.

But God is always good even when he punishes, and he did not abandon his creatures: *The Lord God (Yahweh Elohim) made garments of skin for Adam and his wife and clothed them.* This mysterious detail, strongly tinged with anthromorphisms—and anachronistic as well—undoubtedly indicates that God came to the aid of the guilty pair in order to guide their first steps in the way of the arts. Better still, the Lord allowed these banished ones a glimpse, in the far distant future, of the first feeble rays of a new era, an age of restoration. The climax of this drama was not the end; the action will resume. The trial in the garden had spelled triumph for Satan and the frustration of the divine plan, but the struggles of earth

were finally to terminate in victory for the man and
vengeance for the Creator.

I

The new condition in which man found himself
is characterized by tension.[2] Tension between creature
and Creator: the man fled from the sight of God and
hid himself (Gen 3:10). Internal tension: the man must
now fight against himself so as to gain the mastery
over his now rebellious senses, to check his desires, to
prevent sin from entering into him (Gen 4:7). Domestic tension: the wife would long for her husband and
he would dominate her (3:16). Tension between nature and man: only by hard labor would Adam win
the fruit of his work from thorns and thistles (3:18).
But a special tension existed between mankind and
the serpent:

> *The Lord God (Yahweh Elohim) said to the serpent:*
> > *Because you have done this,*
> > > *cursed are you among all animals*
> > > *and among all beasts of the field;*
> > *On your belly shall you crawl,*
> > > *dust shall you eat,*
> > > *all the days of your life.*
> > *I will put enmity between you and the woman,*
> > > *between your seed and her seed;*
> > *He shall crush your head,*
> > > *and you shall lie in wait for his heel (3:14-15).*

An eternal curse then was to weigh upon the tempter, and the success of the devil will one day be changed into a complete and final defeat. The expression, "to crawl on the belly," retained even in our modern languages, marks his abasement and degradation. What biting irony! The serpent, always represented in Oriental art as erect, or as on a caduceus, twined around a vertical support, was condemned to crawl on his belly! The devil, that vilest and most despised of beings, "will eat (or bite) dust." This same metaphor was used by the scribes who edited the Tell-el-Amarna letters: "May our enemies bite dust."[3]

In the Babylonian hell, "dust is the fare and clay the food" of those who dwell therein.[4] In the biblical narrative these metaphors very naturally serve as an image of the devil, for the sacred author spoke the language of the people. The serpent, symbol of Satan, "eats the dust" either because the reptile seems to feed on the soil with his darting tongue, or because, in the pesudo-science of that period, it actually lived on the dust of the way. In this latter hypothesis the language of the hagiographer would reflect the popular opinion. Ought we to go further and suppose that our account makes use of folklore traditions concerning the serpent's origin? According to these myths the Dragon originally had feet, like the higher animals, and may have eaten grass and foliage; subsequently it was demoted to a serpent, reduced to crawling in the dust and licking it.[5] It is, of course, impossible to prove that such popular legends did exist; we can afford to ignore them. Even if they were proved, we would only conclude from them that they gave some color to the sentence of condemnation. And the sentence itself is clear: the accursed serpent is doomed to contempt and defeat; but his final ruin will only come at the end of a long battle.

God himself leads the struggle, foments the opposition: "I will put enmity. . . ."

Some critics discern nothing more here than an expression of the woman's natural, instinctive repugnance towards snakes. But they minimize the meaning of the Hebrew word translated as *enmity,* which in the Bible always signifies a *hostility between rational beings,* e g, Num 35:21-22; Ezech 25:15, 35:5. Moreover, they do not properly estimate the open declaration of war and its special, extraordinary, divine character. At the very moment Yahweh thunders forth the sentence against the serpent the hostilities begin; the tense of the Hebrew verb often rendered by a future can, as all scholars agree, be equivalent to a *continued present.* War was touched off on God's initiative and it was to continue into the future. A tenacious hatred will pit the **woman** against the devil.

What woman?[6] In the verses immediately preceding and following, "the woman" has consistently designated Eve, and we may assume that the same term refers to the same person here also. Verses 14-15 are a quotation; the chronicler does not speak in his own name, but inserts into his narrative the sentence pronounced by God himself. God did not address our first parents directly when he spoke to the devil, but as Eve, the woman of the preceding verses, was present at the moment of judgment, it is difficult to imagine that the expression did not in some way refer to her. Was she not personally interested in the plan of vengeance? Eve had been tempted and seduced by the infernal serpent, and as a result of her fall had become a friend of the devil, who thus had true dominion over her. From the moment that God pronounced the sentence of condemnation against the devil, however, this friendship was to end, and would turn into enmity. Eve the friend was to become an enemy, and from then on a mortal struggle would rage between the tempted woman and the devil who had deceived her.[7]

This view is borne out by the literary structure of the oracle. The verse in which the punishment of the serpent is promulgated is constructed in the same way as the following verses, where we learn of the punishment of the man and the woman. According to the rhythm of these last two oracles, the guilty ones were punished both by Yahweh and by their victims. The woman's punishment, for example, will come both from God and from her husband; and we should normally expect Eve to participate in the punishment of the serpent who had deceived her.

214

With the majority of the exegetes and many theologians, we find it most probable that the enmity announced by God would set up an opposition between *the first woman* and her seducer. As we shall see, this is not the only enmity so announced, nor the most important; but it is real and fundamental.

*   *   *   *   *

But Yahweh proceeded to enlarge on the sentence and to extend the scope of the struggle; the state of war would not come to an end with the disappearance of the woman who was here and now present. Hostilities were to spread out to include the two camps: "I will put enmity . . . between your seed and her seed."

The first camp was the posterity of the serpent. The exegetes all agree that the phrase has a moral and collective meaning, for the devil does not physically engender sons. His posterity comprises those who resemble him in malice, the evil spirits, accomplices in his revolt and subjected to the same punishment. Does it also include those perverse men who, according to the vivid expression of Saint John (8:44), are "sons of the devil?" Such an addition to the serpent's progeny is not demanded by our text.

In the opposing camp we see the "seed of the woman." What does this expression mean? An individual or a collectivity?

Taken by itself the term, "descendants (or seed) of the woman," can and often does stand for an individual. Thus, at the birth of Seth Eve makes a play on words, crying out: "God (Elohim) has given me (*sath*) another child (seed) in the place of Abel whom Cain slew" (4:25). Of Ismael the Lord says to Abraham, "I will also make the son of the slave girl a great nation because he is your offspring (seed)" (21:13). We must grant, however, that the Hebrew word translated as "seed" almost always refers to a collectivity.

Actually, it is because of the parallelism that we prefer the collective meaning: the "seed of the woman" designates a group. The oracle is logically developed. First, an individual, the woman, is described as the antagonist of the serpent, who is also an individual; the conflict therefore is between two persons. The hostilities then spread, and the human race, Eve's posterity (3:20), attacks another group, the brood of the devil. The earth is transformed into an immense battlefield where men activated by God wage ruthless war against the satanic powers. This unrelenting opposition was to end only with the complete victory of the seed of the woman. With these few words the Bible gives us a profound concept of human destiny, counselling neither a naive optimism nor a resigned pessimism, but an all-out war against a fierce enemy. The resistance advocated springs up immediately after the first defeat. God himself gave the signal for it and undertook to stir up in the hearts of men a hatred toward the children of the devil which will continue until final victory is achieved.

*　　*　　*　　*　　*

The victory is, actually, stated only at the very end: *He (the seed of the woman) shall crush your head, and you shall lie in wait for his heel.* The serpent who tempted the mother of the human race thus reappears at the end of the oracle. As a matter of fact, he has never left the stage, for unlike the woman, who perpetuates herself only through her posterity, the devil, a spiritual and immortal being, subsists personally along with his children. Satan is always pulling strings; he is the tenacious prompter of the diabolical actors who are his children. In the last act he again enters upon the stage, and God informs him of the fate that awaits him.

The serpent, jaws wide open, lies, filled with hatred, in ambush for his enemy; his aim is to bite the heel that is to destroy him. This passage, however, does not merely continue the theme of the mutual hatred of these sworn enemies. Otherwise the tempter would not receive the special punishment which the Creator intends to be meted out to him because of his special guilt; moreover, one who aims at another's head hopes to crush it, whereas one who lies in wait for another's heel only wounds it. Duly appreciating this manifest intention of the Creator, the Vulgate was, in consequence, fully justified in trans-

217

lating the same Hebrew word once as "crush," and in the next phrase by "to lie in wait," that is, to set up an ambush.[8] For Satan is doomed to complete, inevitable defeat. Our text proclaims a victory over the enemy of Eve and her children.

Who, then, will gain the victory? The structure of the oracle in which parallelism plays so predominant a part suggests that there will be *one victor*. The war unfolds as follows: In the first phase, two persons (the woman and Satan) stand opposed; then two groups (the human race and the diabolical brood) confront one another; and finally, one person, the seed of the woman, the agent of the vengeance, is opposed to Satan, the instigator of the fall. Besides, can we not conceive the decisive act of crushing the head of the serpent better, once we see it as the work of one person? But it is difficult to picture the serpent aiming at the heel of a collectivity!

The Hebrew text, in this last member of the sentence, designates the antagonist of the Serpent by the masculine demonstrative pronoun (which the Vulgate translates by *ipsa* instead of *ipsum*). This pronoun clearly refers to the seed (in the Hebrew this noun is masculine), and governs the following verb which is in the singular. According to Hebrew syntax, after a collective noun such as seed, the pronoun and verb referring to it may be in *either* the singular or the plural.[9] The choice of the singular here makes possible the "individualist," "one person" interpretation

218

which the parallelism and imagery of the sentence also suggest.[10]

Here, then, as in the prophecies, the thought glides imperceptibly from general to particular, from collective to individual, from implicit to explicit; the descendant who rises on the horizon, in the last line, was included somehow in the preceding line, in the human collectivity (cf Deut 18:15).

Considering only the rules of historico-critical exegesis, the following conclusions can be drawn from the text:

1 Thanks to God's intervention, Eve ceases to be Satan's ally, and becomes his enemy. The victim will have a part in the punishment of her seducer, although she will not personally achieve the final victory.

2 The hostility will pass on from Eve to her posterity, the mother transmitting to her children her hatred for the diabolical powers. But God himself will conduct the war. Satan had worked for the ruin of humanity; God in his turn, through the enmities which he would arouse, will work for the rout of the devil and his accomplices.

3 Finally, the seed of the woman will triumph. *How?* And *when?* The text does not permit us to answer these questions with certainty. By whom will the Dragon be vanquished? The conqueror will be a member of the human race.

II

A divine oracle may be made clear in two ways: by later, clearer texts, and by its fulfillment.

In the vast perspective of the divine plan, later stages teach us the meaning and orientation of the earlier ones; more recent oracles clarify and complete the older ones. It is thus that God, the author of the whole of the Scriptures, explains his own words and gives us their true meaning.[11] On the other hand, a prophecy proposed in vague and obscure terms is made luminous by comparison with the event which is its fulfillment.[12] "Theological" exegesis thus enriches historico-philological exegesis.

We know with certainty that *one born of a woman* (Gal 4:4) gained a decisive victory over the devil and so avenged the defeat in the garden of Eden. In Jesus the ancient prophecy was splendidly fulfilled. He was the living antithesis of the devil (John 14:30), and his mission in life was to dispossess Satan of the Kingdom usurped by him: "to this end the Son of God appeared that he might destroy the works of the devil" (I John 3:8). The formidable duel in which Christ was engaged with the age-old enemy of mankind came to an end with the crushing of the serpent. "Now," said the Savior on the eve of his death, "now will the prince of the world be cast out" (John 12:31). The victory was dearly bought. All during Jesus' public ministry the devil pursued him, stirring up persecutions against him, raising doubts as to his intentions. Christ generously endured all these sufferings and finally offered his life to his heavenly Father in expiation for the sins of the human race.[13] How often was his heel not bruised!

Between the prophecy and its fulfillment, several of the prophets had traced out the features of the conqueror and permitted a glimpse of his person. The *Liberator* was to belong to the tribe of *Juda*, to be a *descendant of David*, to be *born of a virgin* and *at Bethlehem*, and he was to *ransom his brethren* at the cost of his *sufferings*.[14]

Instructed by these prophecies and enlightened especially by the facts of Gospel history, several of the Fathers (Justin, Irenaeus, Cyprian, Epiphanius, Leo the Great, for example) have interpreted the prophecy of Genesis in a Christological sense.[15] Their opinion corroborates the interpretation we have given above, but does not make it obligatory, for these Fathers do not constitute the whole of Catholic tradition. (Great Doctors of the Church like Cyril of Jerusalem, Basil, Gregory of Nazianzen, John Chrysostom, Cyril of Alexandria, Jerome, and Gregory the Great give no indication that they were aware of such an interpretation.) But with the Fathers of the first group we hold that the last words of the oracle bear literally, immediately, and directly on the person of the **Redeemer**, containing as they do the first announcement made to men

of the good news of salvation, the *Proto-evangelium.**
From the very beginning, God "showed in advance,
clearly and openly, the merciful Redeemer of the human race" (*Ineffabilis Deus*).

*   *   *   *   *

What light does later history cast upon the struggle
between the human race and the powers of evil? Nothing is easier to prove by facts than the continued
hatred of the devil and his angels for men, but it is
very difficult to prove from history the enduring enmity of the seed of the woman towards the children
of Satan. Instead of implacable hatred there have
been many abdications and shameful compromises; the
children succumb to seduction as did their mother before them. The book of Genesis alone is a record of
more defeats than of victories; Eve's posterity resembles less an army of conquerors than a mass of conquered men. At the head of the line marches Eve's
first-born, Cain, "who was of the evil one" (I John 3:12).
The contagion of sin was propagated much more effectively than was that of the good: "The Lord (Yahweh) saw that the wickedness of man on the earth

---

*As the word *evangelium* (or "gospel") means "good
tidings," *Protoevangelium* means "the first good tidings."
It is a reference to Gen 3:15, where, soon after the Fall, a
Redeemer was promised to Adam and Eve.

was great, and that man's every thought and all the
inclinations of his heart were only evil" (Gen 6:5).
"The earth was corrupt, and it was filled with violence" (6:2). "The inclination of man's heart is evil
from his youth" (8:21). Many examples taken from
the Bible could bear out these pessimistic declarations! Every man born of Adam undergoes, like that
first father, the sorrowful experience of good and evil.

We should not, however, stop with only a superficial glance at events, for there is a Christian view of
history. Christ the Redeemer is not only an outstanding member of the human race, nor simply the representative of his brethren; in the fullest sense of the
word he is "the head of all the woman's posterity, of
that posterity which has kept the promise and maintained the enmity with the serpent of old; he has already been the representative of all those who, before his coming, looked towards him and were preserved in their loyalty by faith in him; after his coming he is the head of all who are united to him by
faith and who form with him a single body of which
he is the head."[16]

It is, therefore, not possible for one who looks upon
the unfolding of history with the eyes of faith to iso-
late Christ from the human collectivity. When the
Lord announced that he would place enmity between
the seed of the serpent and the seed of the woman,
he was surely thinking of the children of Eve, but he
discerned Christ among the ranks of men, and Christ

would give the history of Eve's children its true meaning. In Christ that enmity will be fully realized and He will personally crush the head of the serpent. Men were to participate in their leader's war against the devil in varying degrees and with more or less enthusiasm, and with varying success they will aim at Satan so as to crush his head beneath their feet (Rom 16:20). With this in mind we should re-read the eighth chapter of the epistle to the Romans; it is a veritable victory chant of **man united to Christ**.[17]

*   *   *   *   *

Let us return to the first part of the prophecy, "I will place enmity between you and the woman." Following the suggestion of the text and the literary and historical contexts, we have said that Eve is the woman who fights against the serpent. Is this exegesis confirmed by history and later commentaries?

Divine wisdom brings Eve forth from her sin along with the first man (Wisd 10:2). By his merciful pardon God established the first woman in a state of hostility towards the devil, and yet in what follows nothing bears out that condition which the divine oracle announced so emphatically. It has been pointed out that the "mother of all the living" was to undergo punishment for her disobedience (3:16), and that God would come to help her in her need (3:21). For the most part, moreover, whenever Eve is mentioned in the Bible, it is in connection with the fault that attaches to her name.[18] In short, Eve is the woman *through whom sin began.*

The same impression persists in the patristic writings. As far back as Saint Justin and Tertullian the antithesis: **Eve-Mary,** is to be found.[19] In the end this parallelism found expression in the phrase: *"Death came through Eve, life through Mary."* It was oftener the memory of the fallen Eve that attracted the attention of the Fathers than that of the rehabilitated Eve. In this tradition of the churchmen, then, we catch the echo of biblical tradition.

What conclusion may we draw from this? Must we go back on the conclusions of our historico-critical exegesis and reverse the interpretation we gave above, in order to avoid contradicting the prophecy? Are we to say that the oracle was not directed at Eve at all, but at an entirely different person? An out-and-out contradiction would indeed force us to reconsider our analysis of the text, but this is not the case. Once Eve was reconciled to God she did become the enemy of Satan, a fact that all will concede.

But why so emphatically announce an enmity which actually was not very effective? Is this merely an instance of Oriental hyperbole? Several possible explanations are open to us. We can imagine that the splendor of the final victory was reflected in advance upon the first phase of the struggle, and in this way explain the solemnity with which the Lord proclaims

the opening of hostilities. Or we may hold that the
enmity really began with Eve, but not very brilliantly;
and then, with the help of God, hatred of the devil
grew in various degrees among the woman's descendants, to be finally concentrated in its highest degree
and in an absolutely irreducible manner in the heart
of the Redeemer. The war then reached its turning point, and in the combat between Christ and Satan
the seed of the woman crushed the serpent.

This is all very plausible, and God could certainly
have carried out his plan of war in this manner. But
we know, from later revelations, how the divine plan
was in fact accomplished. The Gospel (Luke 1:26 ff,
2:34-35; John 19:26 ff) brings the role of the Virgin
Mary into bold relief. The Old Testament had already outlined her role (Is 7:14; Mich 5:2-3): God
deigned to unite Mary intimately with Christ the Redeemer. Thus, what might have been only hyperbole
with regard to Eve became in the person of Mary a
reality;[20] the Virgin was associated with her Son in
his enmity, in his struggles, and in his victory.

The Fathers and writers of the Church came only
gradually to explore the riches of the Gospel texts
and of the apostolic tradition, and we can trace considerable progress in the Marian interpretation of
Genesis 3:15. The text which today seems to us to
summarize the whole of Mariology attracted little attention on the part of the ancients. Many of the Fathers liked to contrast the roles played by Eve and by

Mary, but these same authors did not trace the contrast to the *Protoevangelium,* and it would be gratuitous to attribute a Marian interpretation of Gen 3:15 to them. *We* are accustomed to contemplate the charming picture of the Virgin, **the Woman and her Seed,** holding the Infant Jesus in her arms and trampling the infernal serpent under foot; *IPSA conteret caput* —"She shall crush his head." But as the text read by the Greek Fathers has the masculine pronoun "he" (i e "autos") instead of "she," they could have imagined such a picture only with difficulty. Saint Ephrem and Prudentius were doubtless the first to apply the last phrase of the prophecy to the Blessed Virgin,[21] and they bear witness to a tradition which would soon, in the 6th century, be asserted in the Vulgate's "**ipsa** *conterest caput.*"[22]

Only slowly, then, were the Fathers and early writers led to discover in the *Protoevangelium,* in a significant formula, their Marian teaching. But their hesitancy (understandable as it is in the circumstances) need not, *must not*—let us thank God!—be ours. For as the sovereign Pontiff assures us, "in this divine oracle God had in advance clearly and openly pointed out the merciful Redeemer of the human race, and had designated his blessed Mother, the Virgin Mary, and at the same time had signally *(insigniter)* expressed the common enmity of the both toward the devil" *(Ineffabilis Deus).*[23] In the *Protoevangelium* Eve is described as having characteristics which belonged first and foremost to Mary, who was associated with the Redeemer in his hatred of the devil and in his victory over him. The enmity mentioned in the prophecy is verified both in Eve and in Mary —really but imperfectly in the one, really and perfectly in the other. Like her Son, an enemy of Satan, militantly opposed to Satan together with her Son, victorious over Satan with and through her Son—such is the Virgin Mary. In the *Protoevangelium* Eve is decked out in Mary's attributes much like those kings of Israel who, in the Psalms, received the praise and prerogatives which belonged to the royal Messiah.

Thus, among the descendants of Eve two personalities emerge: Christ the Redeemer stands out, distinct from the human mass, at the end of the oracle; the other is the Virgin Mary, who, appearing in the wake of Christ, is singled out at the beginning of the prophecy. Perhaps we might better say that it is her attributes that point her out and describe her. We must allow, then, that when God uttered this oracle he included two distinct persons, Eve and Mary, under the one word *the woman*.

How reconcile this conclusion with the rules of philology? The simplest way is to recognize with Coppens that "in the words which the narrator records as pronounced by God or by Adam under the influence of prophetic inspiration, in words which have an oracular aspect and which therefore refer not only to the present but also to the future . . . (the term *woman*) does not formally or primarily refer to Adam's wife, but has a general meaning." It is a universal term, and in its immediate literal sense designates "the female sex in general, Eve and Mary by way of implication."[24]

In order that Mary's enmity be as complete, absolute, unshakeable and enduring as was her Son's, it must imply not only exemption from actual sin but also freedom from original sin from the very first moment of her existence. Furthermore, as Pius XII says in the Bull *Munificentissimus Deus*,[25] Gen 3:15 furnishes a scriptural basis for the Church's faith in Mary's Assumption. Victorious over sin, the Virgin was to be victorious over death. The struggle which the new Eve, in closest union with the new Adam, although hers is a secondary position, wages against the diabolical enemy was to end as the prophetic words of the *Protoevangelium* had foretold, in a complete victory over sin and death, which are ever linked together in the teaching of Saint Paul.[26] "Just as the glorious resurrection of Christ was an essential part and the final sign of this victory, so that struggle which was common to the Blessed Virgin and her divine Son should be brought to a close by the glorification of her virginal body, for the same Apostle says: 'When this mortal thing hath put on immortality, then shall come to pass the saying that is written: Death is swallowed up in victory'."[27]

"Theological" exegesis then corroborates and completes "historico-critical" exegesis:

1   The One who vanquishes the devil is an individual person, as the analysis of the text suggests. Later revelations and ecclesiastical tradition remove all uncertainty on this score: the *Protoevangelium* clearly and openly announces the Messiah-Savior.

2   The war against Satan will be extended to the whole human race, to Eve's posterity; men, united with Christ, will share in the struggle and in the victory of their Head in proportion as they are united to him.

3   Eve really became the enemy of the devil, and through one of her sons triumphs over her deceiver. In the *Protoevangelium* she receives attributes that have been borrowed from another. **The implacable enemy of the devil,** *the* militant and victorious one par excellence, is the immaculate Virgin Mary, now glorified in heaven.[28]

III

Before bringing this study to a close let us attempt to determine, at least in a general way, the literary form of the accounts just analyzed.

If we are to appreciate these chapters properly, we must first of all set them in their proper place in the general framework of Genesis, for they are not a disconnected section but part of a coherent whole. After the author had spoken of the *generation* of the world (ch 1-2), he recorded the progressive *degeneration* of humanity (3:11). Man plunged ever more deeply into sin: murder (4:8), revenge (4:23-24), perversion (4:19-24; 6:5, 11, 13), pride (11:1-9) took up their abode upon earth. At the same time death, with its cortege of suffering and pain, weighed more and more heavily on man, and his life-span sensibly decreased (compare ch 5 and 11:11 ff). Thus, the penalty of death was borne from the beginning and was effective. The situation called for a *regeneration*. With the call of Abraham (Gen˙ 12), God, faithful to his promise, inaugurated his redemptive work and undertook the task of restoration, and set about the task of regrouping dispersed and hostile men by means of the father of believers and of the people of Israel (12:50).

This rapid survey shows that the events narrated in Genesis 2-3 fit into a series of connected facts which are part of a **history**. These chapters "pertain to history in a true sense, which, however, must be further studied and determined by exegetes."[29] Without doing violence to the author's purpose, then, one *cannot* liken these accounts to those purely fictitious narratives which, under the guise of history, aim only at illustrating truths of a moral, social, anthropological, or a religious nature. We do not, however, deny the prophetical and sapiential worth of the old text. The history of the man in Eden foreshadows the destiny of the sons of man. Much more than profane history does it deserve to be called, in Cicero's phrase, the *magistra vitae*,[30] for it governs our religious attitude towards a good, just and merciful God.

In his reconstruction of what happened in Eden, our historian, because of the considerable lapse of time separating him from the beginnings, could not make use of documents that went back as far as the events, nor could he record the reminiscences of the actors or spectators there present, as is obvious in the case of the creation of the man and the woman. He had therefore to draw upon his imagination for a setting, and he did so in accordance with the popular scientific notions and traditions of his time. He had no intention of furnishing us with circumstantial details concerning the appearance of the first human beings. He wished to teach us the divine origin of man and of his nature, his relation to God, his place in the hierarchy of beings, and the respective roles of the man and the woman.

There is also some imaginative thinking in this description of the earthly paradise. The marvelous oasis of Eden resembles the orchard of a Palestinian peasant, but it is embellished and idealized by borrowings from the Babylonian tradition. A comparison with Semitic literature with its trees of life, Cherubim, thunderbolts, etc, does not permit any doubt on this score. The Mesopotamian color is even more accentuated in the accounts of the deluge and the tower of Babel.

Did the author insert fragments of earlier documents into his text? Despite its minute analyses literary criticism cannot furnish us with any certain conclusions here.[31] The thread of the narrative is sometimes interrupted, but it is quickly taken up again; the formulas which seem to be doublets are perhaps nothing more than a mark of the popular narrative style. Though it is not perfectly homogeneous, the account of paradise and the fall as we read it today must be considered as a unit.

There are, also, elements of fiction in the presentation of the actors. Yahweh Elohim deliberates, speaks and acts like a man. The serpent is used as a symbolical mask for the evil Power which opposes the plan of the Creator and seeks the ruin of the man. According to our author sin and death do not enter into the world by the doing of Adam alone; they come from a deeper source.[32] When man came upon the scene the evil spirit was already at work, and it was he who injected trouble into the cosmos and who resisted God's works. Genesis is very discreet about the disturbing activity of the fallen angels. Must it be maintained, as it is by some contemporary exegetes, that by stylizing his account the author also intended, through the medium of the sin of the man, to describe not only the faults of men but also the angelic sin? Or that through the penalties of suffering and death inflicted upon man he meant to imply that disorder was introduced into the cosmos by the rebellion of the spirits? This seems to us to be very subtle, and we shall not venture along that path.

Thus we have allowed for the possibility of creative thinking and for symbolism, both used in the service of history. We are told of facts that are very real facts, and yet, either because of their nature or because the testimony of the actors or spectators involved is unobtainable, they are not presented in all their concrete and individual detail. We seize the **reality** they contain only through these approximations.

How shall we describe so original a literary form? In what category shall we place an account which describes real events by means of literary and symbolical elements? For lack of a more appropriate term, we may designate the whole of Chapters 2-3 as *historical parable*. In referring to them as "parable" we have in mind their figurative element, their dramatic presentation, their setting; and we add the word "historical" to affirm that this literary form deals with real facts. Despite these explanations, the expression may be, perhaps, a bit shocking to some, bringing together as it does words that are apparently mutually exclusive. But then, any violence we may seem to do to ordinary terminology in the present instance serves but to emphasize the disconcerting originality of this marvelous History.

NOTES

1   Tiglath-Pilesar I caused a bronze thunderbolt to be erected on the ruins of Hunusa to forbid the rebuilding of the city: "I fashioned a bronze lightning-bolt, and inscribed thereon the booty I had taken . . . and a decree that the city should not again be inhabited, and that its wall should not again be built. I built a temple of burnt brick in that place and set up therein the bronze lightning-bolt" (Cylinder inscription from Qalaat Shergat, i e, ancient Assur; cf D Luckenbill, *Ancient Records of Assyria and Babylonia*, I, 243, 321).

2   Throughout the whole of the Old Testament we find the bold outlines, summarized here, of man's condition. *Tension between God and man*: the reflex action of fear and flight is classic in the accounts of apparitions (Ex 3:6, 20:19; Judg 6:22; 13:22; Is 6:5); man is conscious of his impurity in the presence of God (Job 4:17-19; Ps 90:3-12; I Kings 8:46; Eccles 7:20; Ecclus 8:5; Prov 20:9). This is why fear penetrates religion. *Internal tension* manifested by a moral disorder: congenital weakness, Gen 8:21; need for education for the correction of the perversion of children's hearts, Prov 22:15. *Domestic tension*: matrimonial difficulties, Ecclus 25:12-25; sufferings of childbirth, Tob 4:4; dismay and shame regarding sex, Lev 12, 15; nakedness inspires contempt and degrades paternal authority, Gen 9:21 ff; and royal authority, II Sam 11:20; priestly, Ex 20:26. *Tension between nature and man*: man works hard to maintain his life.

3   Cf also Is 49:23, 65:25; Mich 7:17.

4 *Descent of Ishtar to the Nether World,* cf *A N E T,* 107a.

5 Cf P Joüon, SJ, "Le Grand Dragon," *R S R* 7 (1927), 444-446; P Humbert, *Etudes,* 186.

6 Cf F Ceuppens, OP, *De Mariologia Biblica* (Marietti, 1951), 5-17; Coppens, "Le Protévangile, Un nouvel essai d'exégèse," *E T L* 26 (1950), 5-36.

7 Cf Bonnetain, "Immaculée Conception," *V D B S,* 246-247.

8 H Pinard de la Boullaye, *Jésus-Messie* (Paris, 1930), 160. Cf J Coppens, *art cit,* 15:
   "I will put enmity between you and the woman
   Between your seed and hers,
   She shall crush your head,
   And you will attempt (but in vain) to bite her in the heel."

9 Gen 1:26.

10 Cf the LXX, which has "autos" (he) instead of "auto" (it); the old Latin versions have "ipse" instead of "ipsum." Cf note 22 *infra.*

11 Cf *supra,* Chap 1.

12 John 20:8-9, 2:19-20.

13 F Ceuppens, OP, *Genèse I-III,* 165.

14 Gen 49:10; Mich 5:1; Is 7:14, 11:1, 53; etc.

15 St Justin: "He . . . was made man of the Virgin, so that the disobedience brought on by the serpent might be cancelled out" (*Dialogue with Trypho,* 100; *P G* 6:709).

   St Irenaeus: "This enmity the Lord recapitulated in himself who was born of a woman and crushes (the devil's) head" (*Advers Haeres* 4, 40:3; *P G* 7:1114).

St. Cyprian: "He had foretold that this seed which would crush the devil's head would come from the woman" (*Advers Jud,* 2:9; *P L* 4:704).

St Epiphanius: "I place enmity . . . yet such a seed of the woman cannot be found. Hence this enmity can be referred to Eve in outline and figure, but not fully and perfectly. But it is actually and fully realized in that holy, singular and outstanding shoot which is from the Virgin Mary alone, without the intervention of any man" (*Advers Haeres* 78; *P G* 42:730).

St. Leo the Great: "God announced to the serpent that the seed of the woman would by its own power crush his poisonous uplifted head—meaning Christ who, born of a Virgin, would pass sentence on the destroyer of the human race" (*Sermo 21, In Nat Dom; P L* 54:194).

16 Bonnetain, *art cit,* 245.

17 Several Fathers have emphasized this collective spirit:

St Ephrem: "(The adversary) is crushed underfoot by those who spurn him and fight against his counsels and plans" (*Lib Attende tibi,* II).

St Ambrose: "He who was the enemy of the good is the common enemy of all, and he is condemned by those whom he has as yet not injured; for whoever injures man—to whom all things are subjected—injures all things. He breaks the common law by which even he is subjected to man along with the other creatures. The curse then burdens him with the common hatred of all" (*De Fuga,* 41; *P L* 14:588).

St John Chrysostom: "Not only the woman alone, but her seed also I declare to be your perpetual enemy. . . . See in this, my beloved, the great care he has for humanity . . . for God humbles him (the serpent) at our feet and allows us to take care [to crush] its head" (*Hom 17 in Gen; P G* 53:143).

St Jerome: "For our steps are impeded by the serpent, and the Lord quickly dispatches Satan beneath our feet" (*Quaest in Gen*, 3:15; *P L* 23:943).

18 Ecclus 25:23; II Cor 11:3; I Tim 2:14).

19 Among the Latins: Tertullian, *De Carne Christi*, 17 (*P L* 2:782); St Augustine, *De Agone Christiano* 22, 24 (*P L* 40:302); St Peter Chrysologus, *Sermo 140, 142 (P L* 52:576, 579). Among the Greeks: St Cyril of Jerusalem, *Catech* 12 (*P G* 33:742); St John Chrysostom, *Homil in Pasch* (*P G* 52:768); Proclus, *P G* 65:751; St John Damascene, *passim*.

20 Pseudo-Jerome: "I admit no other seed of the woman than the one who was, as Saint Paul wrote: *born of a woman.* . . . The Mother of Our Lord Jesus Christ was promised in that other woman. . . . I will place, he said, enmity between you and woman. He did not say *I place* lest this seem to refer to Eve. . . . *I will place*, he said, *enmity between you and woman*—that woman who bore the Savior, not her who gave birth to a murderer" (*Ad amicum aegrotum, Epist* 6; *P L* 30:82 f).

21 St Ephrem: "Hail, O Pure One, you who have crushed the head of the wicked dragon. . . . Hail, O solution of the curse!" (*Omnia opera graece et latine*, III, 547).

Prudentius: "This was that ancient hatred between the viper and man. A fearful rending asunder, for now the prostrate viper is trampled by womanly feet" *Cathemerinon*, Bk III; *P L*, 59:806.

For the Mariological interpretation of Gen 3:15, cf L Drewniak, OSB, *Die Mariologische Deuting von Gen 3:15 in der Väterzeit* (Breslau, 1934); Roschini, "Sull'interpretazione patristica del Protevangelo," *Marianum* 6 (1944), 76-94; Lennerz, "Consensus Patrum in interpretatione mariologica, Gen 3:15," *Gregorianum* 27 (1946), 300 ff; Da Fonseca, "L'Assunzione di Maria nella Scrittura," *Biblica* 29 (1949); T Gallus, *Interpretatio Mariologica Protoevangelii* (Rome, 1949-1954); F Ceuppens, OP, *Mariologia Biblica* (Rome, 1951) 17; A Bea, SJ, "Il Protevangelo nella Traditione Exegetica," *Osservatore Romano,* Dec. 31, 1954). One may here read with profit the opening chapters of *Mary in Our Life* by Father Wm J Most (Kenedy, 1955).

22 The Vulgate here translates the original text incorrectly, without, however, falsifying it. The meaning expressed by this faulty translation (*"She shall crush thy head"*) is not foreign to the text.

23 In this Bull Pope Pius IX did not *define* the authentic sense of Gen 3:15, nor did he teach that there was a universal consent of the Fathers in the Marian explanation of the *Protoevangelium.* Cf Lennerz, "Duae Quaestiones de Bulla 'Ineffabilis Deus'" *Gregorianum* 24 (1943), 347-366.

24 *Le Protévangile,* 28-32. Cf L Cerfaux, J Coppens, J Gribomont, *Problèmes et méthodes d'exégése théologique* (Desclée de Brouwer, 1950), 45-77. This *general meaning* appears again in Gen 2:23-24. Moreover, it will be noted that in Gen 3:16, 17, 19 the prediction extends not only to the first man and the first woman, but to the whole of humanity. The terms *man* and *woman* have in these two sentences a universal meaning.

25 "We must remember especially that, since the second century, the Virgin Mary has been designated by the holy Fathers as the new Eve, who, although subject to the new Adam, is most intimately associated with him in that struggle against the infernal foe which, as foretold in the *Protoevangelium,* finally resulted in that most complete victory over sin and over death which are always mentioned together in the writings of the Apostle of the Gentiles." Cf *The Thomist* 14 (1951), 19.

26 Rom 5-6; I Cor 15:21-26, 54-57.

27 *The Thomist, loc cit,* 20.

28 Cf Coppens, *Les Harmonies des Deux Testaments* (Casterman, 1949) 37 f, 66 f.

29 *Humani Generis,* # 38.

30 Cicero, *De Oratione,* II, 9. The phrase means that history teachs us how we should live.

31 For an exposition and criticism of the most recent theories of Rutgers, Begrich, Mowinckel, Michelet, Zimmerli, Humbert, Lods, cf Coppens, *La Connaissance. . . .,* 49-72, and his "L'unité littéraire de Genèse 1-3," *E T L,* 27 (1951), 91-99; R A Mackenzie SJ, "Before Abraham Was . . .," *C B Q* 15 (1953), 131 ff; J L McKenzie, SJ, "The Literary Characteristics of Genesis 2-3," *Th S,* 15 (1955), 541-572.

32 Wisd 2:24: "By the envy of the devil, death came into the world."

CHAPTER SIX

Practical Applications

Whenever I have lectured on the subjects we have been considering, I have noticed two markedly divergent reactions on the part of my audiences. One group betrays its obvious relaxation and relief; the other, a sort of shocked surprise that is sometimes accompanied by fear. The first reaction is usually that of high school and college teachers; the second, of those who teach the lower grades.

This different audience-reaction can easily be explained. High school and college teachers have to deal with young people who are of an independent turn of mind and are critical—and at times hypercritical—by reason of their recently acquired smattering of scientific knowledge, and also, perhaps, because of the derisive remarks of their "emancipated" companions.

When, then, these instructors attempt to explain the difficult passages of the Sacred Scriptures to their students, they find some of them of a decidedly unreceptive frame of mind. Hard-pressed to defend the strictly historical explanation of the first pages of the Bible, these teachers readily accept those broader interpretations which will enable them to cope with their youthful challengers.

Those who teach in the lower grades are in a wholly different position. The simple, imaginative children of grammar school age find no difficulty in the story of the creation of the world in six days, or in God's fashioning man out of clay, like a potter, or in his making the first woman from one of Adam's ribs, or in the fact that a real serpent spoke and induced the woman to eat the "apple." A strictly historical explanation of the account of how all things began satisfies the young —at least temporarily; their minds are fond of images and marvels. Their teachers consequently do not feel the utility or even the necessity of revising the instruction which they themselves received and which they think is traditional. Many of them are frightened by novelty, which seems to them to spell the collapse of an irreplaceable, age-old edifice, and they at once tremble at the objection: "Religion is a changing thing!" What they do not take into account is the difference between the essentials and the accidentals in the Genesis account, and the fact that the differences in interpretation bear only on the accidentals.

No one in his right mind would recommend that, because of certain real difficulties, or in order to conform to the modern temper, we should plunge headlong into innovations, or allow ourselves to be naively impressed by theories that flourish today and are gone tomorrow. However embarrassing difficulties may be, they do not under any circumstance permit us to sacrifice the truths of revelation, to abandon sound theological conclusions, or to deviate from the directives of the Teaching Authority of the Church. Difficulties help keep us on our toes and prompt us to distinguish more carefully between the revealed truth—its essential, permanent, intelligible meaning—and the concrete, figurative covering under which the Holy Spirit was pleased to transmit his message.

As a matter of fact, some aspects of our catechetical teaching should be corrected. Guitton writes: "It is imprudent to an extreme to propose as historical reality certain symbols that are but the envelope of religious truth, as, for example, the creation of the woman from the man's *rib*, or the eating of the forbidden *fruit*. . . . At school, and very often at home as well, the child lives in an environment which can no longer boast the simple, tranquil faith of former times, and which, rightly or wrongly, thinks itself to be enlightened. Give a child of ten the idea that the fruit of paradise, or the days that elapsed before the stars were created, have as much reality as the wood of the Cross, or the resurrection of Jesus, or the multiplication of the loaves, and the doubts which he cannot fail to have about his fairy-tale wonders may be transferred to the miracles or events narrated in the Gospels. A young man may even lose his faith because he has identified that faith with certain Oriental expressions which were meant to make a religious truth understandable to his forefathers, who in certain respects were more childlike than he."[1]

"Beginning with the very first instruction on the biblical account of primitive history, therefore, we must take care not to create false pictures and concepts in regard to these events. If we deliberately set out to induce belief in all the external details of the narrative, we are only preparing for the later loss of confidence in the truthfulness of the Scriptures. Then we shall have to explain later difficulties (which will inevitably arise) by saying: 'Why, the text does not mean that at all!' Explanations of this sort come too late when they come only as answers to objections. Of course, when our young people first come into contact with the Old Testament, we cannot immediately explain all the fine points to them. But from the very beginning we must give them a *general idea* of the divinely revealed Old Testament, an idea that is capable of adjustment and development, one that will grow in depth with the passage of time, with the help of fuller explanations, and with a deeper study of the principal problems."[2]

We simply must not allow our children to think that man was created by God "four thousand years ago" or "about four thousand years ago," or that according to the Bible the world was made in "six" periods, no more, no less. It is dangerous to declare without any reservations that the Creator molded a human statue out of clay; our listeners will think of vacationers sculpting sand figures on the beach. It would be equally awkward to insist on the exact nature of the forbidden "fruit"; the Bible does not call it an apple.* Finally, it is not good pedagogy to give the same importance to everything in the biblical account. Curious and picturesque details might distract the child from the essentials.

What, then, is to be done? What shall we say, and what leave unsaid? How is the teacher to express himself? This is a difficult and delicate problem, so let us approach it with prudence and discretion, *and with a filial submission to the directives of the Church*.

The statement of the history of our beginnings should be the work of a team, the result of the collaboration of theologians, exegetes, scientists and educators. Without theology the exegete will stray into

---

*According to a Jewish tradition, the "fruit" was either *grapes*, or *olives*, or *wheat*. The Greeks thought it was a *fig*, the Latins, an *apple*. None of these traditions is conclusive, none important. It may be noted, as a suggestive curiosity, that the Latin word for *apple* is the same as that for *evil*, **malum**.

doctrinal rashness; without sound exegesis, the theologian is liable to move about in the realm of the *a priori;* without some scientific knowledge both the theologian and the exegete may reveal a naiveté lacking in broadness of vision. Finally, how can anyone, without the help of educators familiar with the psychology of children, write a history suitable to the understanding of young minds?[8]

Fully cognizant of our insufficiency in the matter, we make the following suggestions.

I

We ought, it would seem, to distinguish *three levels* of teaching: that of the grammar school level, that of the discussion group, and that of the pulpit.

With regard to the **grammar-school level**, the explanation of the first chapters of Genesis should be progressive, homogeneous in all its phases, keeping the essential separate from the accidental, the certain from the uncertain, the imagery from the idea.

* * * * *

First of all our commentary should be *progressive.* The intellectual equipment of a child is not as complete as that of an adolescent, nor that of an adolescent as developed as that of an adult. We must take both intellectual capacity and subject matter into account. This is the A B C of pedagogy. But is this elementary rule always observed? What good is accomplished by mentioning the "six days" when telling the story of creation to little children? Incapable as they are of understanding the setting, they will naturally think that the world was created in six days of twenty-four hours each, and thus will from the outset be started off in the wrong direction. On the other hand, the teacher will present the narrative of Genesis to the more advanced student as it stands, and will briefly explain the sense and meaning of the "six days."

In describing what happened in the earthly paradise we should first of all emphasize God's goodness. The Creator wanted our first parents to be perfectly happy, and that is the basic significance of the description of Eden. This primitive happiness depended on obedience to the divine precept. Deceived by the envious devil, man upset God's plan by committing sin. Let us not fail to set before the minds and hearts of our children—and from the very first—the beloved figure of the Redeemer.

"Not that we simply pass over the images used in the opening chapters of the Bible, for they will always find a home in the Church, but we should stress the teaching contained in them. What is being taught is more important than the images used to teach it; images are made to serve the teaching. We must in-

struct the child that the important thing—what he
ought to retain, and what the Bible teaches—is not the
'forbidden fruit' or the 'serpent,' but the spiritual
drama being enacted in the souls of Adam and Eve.
Not to do this is to be fundamentally untrue to the
Bible and to the literal sense of the Bible, which here
teaches a truth of the spiritual and moral (but not the
scientific) order. The Bible has a message for the mind
as well as for the imagination. Let us add that it would
be disastrous . . . to teach the child or even to allow
him to believe that the scene of the second chapter
of Genesis took place exactly as did the scene on
Calvary."[4]

Let us be careful of the expressions that we use.
Thus, in reference to the serpent we might say, "To
designate the devil, the Bible speaks to us of a serpent.
. . . It was to make known to us that our first parents
could *not die* that God brings to our attention the
presence of the tree of life in the middle of the garden." It would serve no purpose to pronounce *ex pro-
fesso* on the reality or non-reality of these mysterious
trees, as these details are now being freely discussed
by exegetes. Indeed, it would be imprudent, and perhaps dangerously so, if one were to bring up these
exegetical controversies in the presence of the little
ones. Children, like the uninstructed laity, would not
understand the nuances of our interpretation and might
perhaps be scandalized. Instead of diffusing light,
then, we should be sowing trouble in others' minds:

"And through their 'knowledge' the weak one will perish, the brother for whom Christ died" (I Cor 8:11).

But the primary teacher should keep abreast of the general trends of modern biblical science, so as to know as clearly as he can the exigencies and the limits of orthodoxy. Such knowledge is all the more indispensable for the teacher who must conduct higher courses in religion, or who directs a discussion group.

❖   ❖   ❖   ❖   ❖

Our exposition of the Bible should be *homogeneous*. At every level, whether elementary, high school, or college, our teaching should be consistent. In the elementary course, let us avoid filling the minds of children with examples, notions, and ideas which will later have to be retracted in the upper grades or higher courses. Many young people are bewildered when they hear a college professor, or lecturer, or radio-orator hold forth about the "millions of years of geological history." How different this is from the four thousand years to which they have been accustomed! No wonder these young people sometimes react strongly and demand to know, "Why were we not told about this before?"

In the interests of homogeneity also, let us not lay too much stress on the molding of the human form when teaching small children, lest we may later have to tell them, when they are older, that this, too, "means something else." Indeed, we should be lucky to have the opportunity to make the correction in time and to set such false or equivocal statements aright because many children are present only for the first years of religious instruction and then break away from the influence of Christian educators. So they are deprived, and often for life, of that further learning which is necessary if they are to revise any equivocal notions absorbed in early childhood. They thus launch forth into life equipped wtih childish ideas about our beginnings. Under the circumstances, how will they be able to defend their faith against the objections and gibes of men opposed to Christian truths?

In order to safeguard the homogeneity of our teaching, let us therefore affirm nothing at the elementary level which we shall have to retract later on on a higher level. However difficult of attainment this ideal is, we must still try to achieve it.

* * * * *

Finally, we must take pains to acquire *theological precision* in our teaching. We must distinguish what is certain from what is uncertain, the essential from the accessory, the idea from the image by which it is made incarnate. The respect due to the word of God demands this of us.

In our teaching we must bring out the certain and profitable content of the Genesis account: God cre-

ated all things; he alone is eternal; the world began
to exist; God created man in a very special manner
in his own image; it was he who formed the man and
the woman, man's helpmate, endowed with the same
nature as he, in view of the propagation of the human
race. On the other hand, we should prudently keep
in the background certain disputed points, such as the
reality or non-reality of the animal-serpent, of the tree
of life, of the tree of knowledge of good and evil,
of the cherubim. If, however, a precocious child should
ask explicit questions on this subject—"Was the serpent a real animal?" or "Do we have to believe this?"
—we must answer without hesitation that our faith
does not force us to say so. But we should immediately add that, whether it was real or unreal, the serpent certainly represents the devil. That is what is
essential here. The same procedure should be followed if we are questioned about the trees of the
garden. Objective or not, these trees stand for historical realities, namely, the condition of our first parents, their happiness, their test.

As things now stand, it is absolutely unnecessary
for us, in the interests of safety, to insist so strongly
on the strictly historical interpretation held at the beginning of the century that our listeners will come to
look upon such an exegesis as the only orthodox solution. Contrariwise, it would be imprudent for one who
holds for modern theories to pour them indiscrimin-

ately into the minds of children in the lower grades, especially as the specialists set forth some of these explanations as hypotheses only, sometimes indeed as mere working hypotheses. In particular, we must be very reserved about the sexual interpretation of the sin in paradise. Some specialists like Father Coppens accord it some probability and importance, holding that the hagiographer took it for granted without formally teaching it. But the specialists are careful not to inculcate the idea in their textbooks.

Finally, it is wrong, even under the pretext of bringing one's teaching down to the level of simple minds, to adopt a policy of "all or nothing," so that in Genesis either "everything is historical" or "nothing is historical." This is a fatal simplification and begets a false security in doctrine which undermines the traditional teaching of the Church!

The teacher, therefore, insofar as it is possible to him, will make every effort to lay hold on the certain teachings of these chapters and to disengage from them those which cannot be historical. The following outline represents an attempt to distinguish between the 'imagery" and the historical reality.

The Imagery	To Be Retained
Yahweh fashions a figure of clay (2:7a).	The body of the man, which is material, was created in a special manner by God.

252

Yahweh breathes his own breath into the man's face (2:7b).	The soul of the man, which is spiritual and immortal, is produced directly by God.
Yahweh extracts one of the man's ribs and makes it into a woman (2:21-22).	Eve is of the same nature as Adam; husband and wife form one being, and the woman is dependent on the man.
Yahweh forms a man and makes a woman (2:7, 22).	Unity of the human race; primitive monogamy.
Yahweh transfers the man into the garden of Eden (2:15).	God elevates man to a state transcending his nature.
The Bible describes this ideal garden, situated in an ideal region (2:8-14).	Our first parents enjoyed perfect happiness.
There the tree of life grows (2:9).	They cannot die.
There Adam reviews the animals and gives them names befitting their natures (2:19-20).	By his intelligence and power, the man has dominion over the animal world.

There Adam converses familiarly with his Creator (3:8 ff).

He is admitted to friendship with God.

A forbidden tree, the tree of knowledge, grows there (3:3).

But this original happiness is made subordinate to man's obedience.

The serpent (3:1) enters into conversation with the woman (3:1-3).

The devil tempts the woman.

The woman, deceived by the serpent, takes and eats of the forbidden fruit (3:6).

The woman, led astray by the devil, succumbs to the temptation and commits sin.

The woman gives the forbidden fruit to the man, who also eats of it (3:6).

The man, tempted by his wife, falls in turn, and sins.

Yahweh expels our first parents from paradise (3: 23).

Intimacy with God and the privileges of sanctity and original justice are lost.

The cherubim and zigzag flames guard the entrance to the garden of Eden (3:24).

This happy state is definitively lost for the human race.

But the "seed of the woman" will crush the head of the serpent (3: 15).

But a Savior, the son of the woman, will take revenge upon the serpent-devil.

This parallel shows clearly that Chapters 2 and 3 of Genesis "relate in simple and figurative language, adapted to the understanding of a less developed people, the fundamental truths presupposed for the economy of salvation."[5]

II

The following pages contain concrete *examples* of how the foregoing rules can be put into effect.[6]

Creation

(The first type of lesson, suitable for very small children.)

"Thousands and thousands of years ago there was no light, no sun, no moon, no stars. There were no men nor animals, no plants or stones, not even a tiny grain of sand. (Here the things best known to the children might be mentioned.) None of these things existed. *The world is not eternal.*

Before the world began, God alone existed; there was only God. He always existed and he will always exist. He is eternal."

* * * * *

"Since God is all good and since he can make whatever he wishes—that is why we say he is 'all-powerful' —he decided that the earth should come into existence at a given moment, together with everything that it contains, as well as the sun and moon and stars that shine above us. He willed that there should be heaven and earth.

"No one knows exactly how each thing came into existence in the world, or in what order God produced the things we see, or how long he took to perform the wonders of heaven and earth. God alone knows this. He could have told us about it, but he did not think it necessary to do so, for we can get to heaven without such knowledge.

"But one thing we do know, something more important and useful than all the others, namely, that God does not need anything or anyone to help him. (Here by means of comparisons the teacher can show the difference between the divine "work" and human work.) All God had to do was to will or command, and what he willed or commanded was done when and as he willed it. God commanded: 'Let there be light,' and light came to be. God willed the blue sky, the earth, the ocean, the sun that shines during the day, and the moon and stars that shine by night. And into existence came the blue sky and the earth and the ocean, and the sun and moon and stars began to shine in the firmament. God willed that there be on the earth all kinds of plants and every kind of animal; and plants pushed up from the earth and animals moved about on the surface of the earth.

"In this way God did not need anything or anybody to help him make heaven and earth; he simply issued a command. Nothing as yet existed when he produced all things. That is why we say that God *created* heaven and earth; he is the **Creator**.

"When God created the heavens and the earth, the plants and the animals, he resolved to place upon earth a living being much more perfect than all the others, namely, man. So he said to himself, 'Let us make man in our image and likeness,' that is to say, an intelligent being and a free one. (Here the teacher might show the difference between man and animals, giving several examples. Under no circumstance should mention be made of the 'souls of animals.' However exactly this philosophical expression may designate the life principle, it will confuse rather than enlighten children if used too early.)

"God willed man to have a body. At the same time he caused a breath of life to enter into the body, an intelligent soul which is free and immortal. (Give examples to bring out the difference between the soul and the body.)

257

"The first man—to whom the Bible gives the name Adam—is the father of all men. In order that he might not be alone, God gave him a companion like himself; he created the first woman. That is why we call Adam and Eve our **first parents**."

❖   ❖   ❖   ❖   ❖

In this account, therefore, there are several important truths to remember:

1. The world did not always exist. Only God who is eternal existed always.

2. Heaven and earth, that is, all things that exist, were created by God. He who is omnipotent commanded, and everything was made; God is the Creator.

3. God is the sovereign Lord of all things. We belong to him, body and soul.

❖   ❖   ❖   ❖   ❖

When teaching more advanced students, we will pay greater attention to the words of the text itself, for our children should be familiar with this famous passage of the Bible. It is at this time, and in our opinion only at this time, that we should draw the child's attention to the meaning of the days of creation. We will already have told him, and deliberately, that God had not intended to teach us the details of creation, particularly its order and duration. The time has now come to go on with his instruction in the same line (*homogeneity*) and to complement it (*progression*), without, however, becoming involved in a rigid literalism. Thus:

"The Holy Scriptures, the Word of God, picture the Creator as working for 'six days' at his great task. It is not put in this way to teach us that God actually created the world in six days of twenty-four hours each, that he made the light on the first day, the firmament on the next, and on the third the earth with its grass and plants and trees, and so on, but for the purpose of teaching us a lesson. After the example of their Master, men shall work six days and then rest on the seventh: 'You must observe Sunday by serving God devoutly.' The Bible says that God rested on the seventh day. This is only a manner of speaking, for God cannot ever become tired. The Bible wishes to tell us simply that God stopped creating."

Should creation be presented from an evolutionary point of view at this stage of the instruction? In our opinion that question may be better taken up later. We do not want to link up our Catholic faith and modern scientific findings. Let us not surrender the Christian message to either creationist or evolutionist theory. In any event, let neither the theologian nor the exegete, nor, above all, teachers of religion take it upon themselves to defend and to propagate the theory of universal evolution. Let us leave this role to the scientists, although we should not become simply indifferent to scientific discoveries in this field.

In the preceding narrative we referred to the cre-
tion of Adam and Eve in a rather vague manner. The
time has now come to develop these elementary notions. Before all else we are to inculcate the doctrine
of the eminent dignity of man. Having a body he
resembles the animals; there is something perishable
about him; he is dust. That is why the Bible story
represents God as taking our body from the dust of
the earth. Let us use this example to point out to the
children that all the words of the Bible are not necessarily to be taken in their strictest sense. God is a
spirit, he has no hands. If then the Bible uses such
language, it is for the purpose of teaching us that by
the special intervention of divine power the first man
received a material, earthly, perishable body. But man
has something else that sets him apart absolutely from
the animals, something whereby he resembles God
himself. Intelligent and free, Adam is the image of
God. In order to bring out our grandeur and nobility,
God breathed into the man's face; our soul is immaterial, divine, imperishable.

Apropos of the woman, two essential ideas should
be brought out in our teaching: man and woman are
of the same nature, and Eve is the companion of
Adam. Both are destined, in marriage, to live together
and to form but one heart and one mind.

It would be well to say nothing for the moment
about the precise manner of Eve's creation. Further
information may be reserved for later. If, however,

it seems good to say a few words about it, we might express ourselves something like this: "God willed that the first woman be formed from the very being of Adam"; or better: "God willed the first woman to be created in the image of Adam." And if some precocious child asks about the rib, let us reply that our faith does not oblige us to accept this detail.

At this point in the story of the creation of Adam and Eve, we might bring up, briefly, the question of the age of man. We should be deliberately vague in our expression: "Much more than four thousand years ago" or "Probably thousands and thousands of years ago." We should abolish from our teaching all mention of "four thousand years" or "about four thousand years." We should indicate and praise the work done by scientists whose function it is to seek out the details and to discover the order and duration of the formation of the world. This is a good way to root out from the mind of the child the myth of the opposition existing between faith and reason. But at the same time, as a prudent precaution, we should point out that science has its limits and can go only so far.

The Earthly Paradise

"God willed man to be happy on earth. Because he loved them, God created Adam and Eve in a state of *perfect happiness* which we find hard to imagine, since we live in an unhappy world. Notice how God proceeds to give us an idea of this happiness of Adam and Eve; he describes for us the earthly paradise, a spot on the earth which is so beautiful that it makes us think of the heavenly paradise.

"This description is based on reality. The earthly paradise was a wonderful garden, a rich and fertile place where trees of every kind grew. This is an effective way to suggest that nothing was lacking to our first parents.

"Adam and Eve could not die. Because of this privilege the day was to come when, without having to suffer the agonies of death, they would enter the paradise of heaven, there to see and love God forever. To help us understand that it was the Creator's intention that Adam and Eve live forever and never die, the Holy Scripture tells us about a tree planted in the garden of Eden. It had a very mysterious name; it was the 'tree of life.'

"God treated our first parents as a father treats his beloved children. Between him and them there was friendship and peace.

"Thus, Adam and Eve enjoyed such complete happiness that they could not have desired anything better. They were privileged persons. But not only they, for Adam and Eve were to transmit this great happiness to all their children, just as wealthy parents leave inheritances to their children. This was by divine favor, because God loves men and he wants them all to be happy.

"But there was one *condition,* and God had a perfect right to impose it upon them, because he is their Creator, Master and Father. This condition was: 'Do not commit sin—that is, do not disobey me.' 'You may eat of the fruit of every tree in paradise,' the Lord had said, 'but you must not touch the fruit of the tree of knowledge of good and evil.' In other words, 'You must not commit sin, you must not disobey.' The command was clear and plain. As a sign of this prohibition, Holy Scripture notes the presence in the garden of another mysterious tree, the tree of knowledge of good and evil.

"What will our first parents do? Will they respect the command of their Master and Father, or will they pay no attention to it? *Will they obey or disobey?*"

❖　＊　＊　❖　＊

In this account two truths are to be retained:

1. When God created our first parents he wanted man to be perfectly happy, in soul and in body.

2. Our first parents could keep this happiness on one condition, by not committing sin, by not being disobedient. A single sin and everything was lost.

We have especially insisted throughout on those "fundamental truths which underlie the economy of salvation." In this way we prepare the child to appreciate the role of the Redeemer. The realistic description of the Bible is made to serve the idea. If in order to explain the first chapters we make use of pictures, we are not to forget that the *teaching* is the principal thing.

Furthermore, we have so expressed ourselves that we need not be afraid of having to retract any part of it in the future. Whether the biblical description of paradise is objective or not, these facts will always remain true:

1) The Scriptures make use of this kind of language in order to suggest to us the idea of the perfect happiness of our first parents;

2) this description is based on reality;

3) the Scriptures speak of the tree of life in order to let us understand that Adam and Eve could *not* die;

4) "do not eat the fruit" means "do not commit sin."

In the upper grades or in high school, circumstances may indicate a more explicit handling of the trees of the garden, and this can be done without entering into any controversial details about them. Our students will not be able to follow such arguments, and we might thereby disturb them to no purpose. We should then limit ourselves to something like this: "Was there really a tree in the earthly paradise which produced immortality? We are not sure. The tree may be purely symbolical. But *what is certain* is that God wished to point out to us the fact that it was possible for our first parents *not to die*." A similar explanation can be given for the "tree of the knowledge of good and evil."

We should not linger long over these questions with children present, lest we seem to invest the problem with an importance it does not have.

The Temptation

"God did not create only man. He had also given life to other beings called angels. These angels do not have a body as we do; they are spirits. Not all of them remain good; some, the devils, are wicked. Their leader is Satan.

"Now Satan is God's enemy, and he is jealous of man's happiness. This is why he tried to make our first parents commit sin. We call this a *temptation*.

"This is how the Holy Scripture tells of that temptation: Eve heard the evil spirit, Satan, saying to her: 'Is it true that God has forbidden you to eat the fruit of the trees that are in the garden?'

"Eve should have chased the evil spirit away, for no one should ever enter into conversation with the devil. But she imprudently answered, 'We have permission to eat of all the trees; we are forbidden only to eat the fruit of the tree of the knowledge of good and evil.'

265

"This was true; our first parents could do whatever they pleased, short of committing sin by being disobedient.

"Eve continued her conversation with Satan, 'God has forbidden this to us, and he has told us that if we eat of it we shall die.'

"'Die? Not at all!' And the devil, being a liar besides being jealous, sowed doubt and pride into Eve's heart, 'Do not believe what God has told you. If you do what he has forbidden you to do, you will become like him and you will not be forced to obey him any longer.'

"Then Eve became proud. She desired the forbidden fruit, that is, sin. Suddenly she yielded, tasted the forbidden fruit, committed sin. Then she in her turn tempted Adam, and he also succumbed to the temptation, and like his wife, disobeyed seriously and revolted against God.

"The devil had conquered; he destroyed God's work, he made our first parents miserable. He had won the round."

* * * * *

From this account we can conclude:

1. The devil, the enemy of God and of man, tempted our first parents.

2. Adam and Eve succumbed to the temptation, and seriously disobeyed their Lord and Father. Pride was the sin that overthrew them.

We have deliberately not mentioned the word serpent, so as not to give our children any grounds for believing that the story just told them resembles one of Aesop's fables. Not that the teacher should not speak of the serpent at all; he simply should be careful not to be too realistic. It will be enough if he chooses his words carefully: "The serpent, that is, the devil." This statement is perfectly true, whether the serpent was a real animal taken over by the devil, or a simple snakelike apparition, or merely a symbol. But we should shun all descriptions in which the serpent is represented as "stretching out his neck so as to start a conversation," or in which "reasons" are given "why Eve was not frightened by this great serpent." If a child should ask why the snake represents the devil, let us not proceed to spout off the names of all the serpent-gods in Babylonian literature; only specialists would be impressed. Let us simply say that the serpent represents the devil because he crawls along, hides, and strikes without warning. This is a plausible explanation. The more curious and alert may be told that the serpent was frequently associated with the pagan gods whom the Scriptures refer to as "devils," and as a result the serpent was a particularly suitable "front" for the diabolical tempter.

As regards the different phases of this devilish temptation, it is easy to bring this home to children, for despite their tender years they have already experienced the allure of forbidden fruit!

The Punishment

"God is good. But he is also just. That is why he punishes people when they are guilty of sin.

"Almost as soon as our first parents had disobeyed they felt a great change in themselves. No more joy, as before; deep down in their hearts they felt sadness, grief, uneasiness, defiance. No one is happy after he sins. Before their disobedience Adam and Eve had lived in peace with God. But now they are afraid; they want to hide. As if a man could hide from God, who sees and knows all, even our most secret thoughts!

"What a change!

"God called out to the man, 'Adam, where are you?'

"Adam replied, 'Lord, when I heard your voice I was afraid and I hid.' How is it possible not to be afraid when in the state of sin? The just God always punishes those who disobey him.

"And God asked, 'What have you done that you are afraid and are ashamed? Have you perchance eaten of the forbidden fruit?'

"But Adam tried to defend himself instead of admitting his disobedience. 'The woman whom you gave me as my companion gave me some fruit and I ate it.' Adam tries to shift the blame for his fault on the woman. How base of him! What is more, he seems to be blaming God himself! What ingratitude!

"Then God asked the woman, 'What have you done?'

"And she, instead of admitting her guilt, accused the devil, 'The devil deceived me.'

"God then becomes the judge. He condemns the three guilty ones: the devil, Eve, Adam. To the devil he said 'Cursed are you!' This is the worst of punishments; between God and the devil no friendship or reconciliation is possible.

"Then God spoke to Eve, "Your children will cause you much care and suffering, and you will be under the domination of your husband.' But God did not curse Eve.

"Finally, God spoke to Adam, 'Because of your sin the earth will be accursed, it will bear thorns and thistles for you. You will eat your bread by the sweat of your brow until the day your body returns to the earth out of which it was taken, for dust you are and unto dust you will return.'

"The earth was cursed, but not Adam. Still, the man was condemned to work laboriously at the task of growing things. He was to suffer fatigue, to be sick, and in the end, to die. And this punishment was to fall on all the children of Adam and Eve."

*   *   *   *   *

Here there are three important lessons to be retained:

1. Sin is the cause of all suffering and of death.

2. The punishment affects all men, who are born sinners.

3. God is infinitely good.

God's Vengeance

"The devil had won. But not for always, for God is never overcome. Our first parents were punished; they had merited punishment. But they were going to obtain forgiveness, for God, who is just, is also a Father whose love knows no bounds. As a matter of fact, Adam and Eve had no sooner lost their wonderful privileges than God promised them a great blessing.

"God said to the devil, "I will place enmity between you and the woman; her son will crush your head.'

"This means: 'I shall send someone to conquer you, Satan.' This conqueror is our Savior, our Lord Jesus Christ. He shall be the leader of all men and will undertake the war against Satan. In company with him we shall all be able to triumph over the devil. Together with Jesus, the Blessed Virgin, his Mother and ours, will crush the head of the devil.

"Thus, joy again found a place in the hearts of our first parents. They knew that God forgave them and that one day they and their children would again see the Lord in the paradise of heaven."

*　*　*　*　*

Our of this account we may retain these truths:

1. God did not forsake sinful man, but announced to him the "good news" of the coming of a Redeemer.

2. God's mercy is infinite.

In explaining this profoundly psychological narrative, so full of religious truth, the teacher will do his utmost to awaken the moral sense of his young charges. The story of Eden provides him with a rich material that is relatively easy to handle: the joy and peace of the obedient man, the sadness and remorse of sinners; sin is "bad for man" and displeasing to God; to admit one's sins takes courage; the utter futility of excuses in God's presence; the value of repentance; finally and above all, the goodness, justice, mercy of God.

III

Discussion groups provide the opportunity to put the text in its proper setting, to give explanations, defend one's positions, and go into detail in a way not possible in a class in religion. Such groups call for much prudence, a solid exegetical and theological training, and a sufficient background of general information. The leader of a discussion group, however, will feel less like a tight-rope walker fearful of leaning too far either to the right or to the left; it was very difficult, when dealing with such delicate subjects, to hit upon the exact phrase that was suitable to simple minds. This difficulty is not so great in discussion groups, although it does not completely disappear. No one should feel that he is dispensed from the theological disciplines and hence free to give utterance to extravagant views.

The utmost circumspection is especially called for when treating of scientific questions which have a bearing on the truths of the faith. Certain of these hypotheses may have scientific foundations, but they are to be accepted with prudence. The relationship between these hypotheses and the *deposit of faith* must be carefully defined; the connection may sometimes be rather close, but oftentimes there is none at all. In these matters the faithful retain a liberty that is rather wide and sometimes even absolute. The age of the human race, for instance, is not of itself necessarily bound up with dogma. The animal origin of the human *body* (with the restrictions noted above) is still, in the present state of the sciences and theology, subject matter for free discussion and study on the part of the scientists. We must still examine the arguments advanced for and against these views, and pass judgment on them "with the necessary seriousness, moderation and measure, and provided that all are prepared to submit to the judgment of the Church, to whom Christ has given the mission of interpreting authentically the Sacred Scriptures and of defending the dogmas of faith." The question of polygenism, on the other hand, is *de se* connected with Catholic doctrine, and involves the question of original sin. It is in no way apparent how it can be reconciled with that which "the sources of revealed truth and the documents of the Teaching Authority of the Church propose with regard to that sin which proceeds from a sin actually committed by an individual Adam. . . ."[7]

We would do well not to introduce biblical subjects into our discussions until we know that our hearers have a proper understanding of the Church's teaching concerning biblical inspiration, and of the distinction between revelation and inspiration.* Our students will thus be shielded from the tendency to place the Sacred Books on a par with works of classical antiquity, or to confuse the opening pages of Genesis with Platonic myths. We must ever aim at arousing in our students a deep respect and true devotion for the Word of God.

With some slight changes the following outlines can be used by teachers of higher courses of religion.

I. The Bible, the "Word of God."

Points for Discussion

1 How explain the veneration accorded the Gospels at a Solemn Mass? Give some ancient or modern

---

*Everything and every word of the Bible is *inspired* and true, but not everything in it is *revealed*. Inspiration is the divine guarantee of the truth of what the sacred writer says. As a result of inspiration merely human truths may be proposed in all their modalities; whereas in the case of revelation the sacred writer is more the mere oracle of God, repeating what God makes known to him.

historical examples of the respect shown toward the Bible.

2 What makes the text of the Bible sacred? Is it sacred for the same reason that the text of the Catechism, or of devotional books like the *Imitation* are considered "holy?" What makes the difference?

3 Is the Bible a human product? Name some of its "authors." Note the very human variety of its literary forms and styles. Search out some of them in your daily Missal.

4 Does the human quality of the Bible exclude its divine character? In this regard, consider our belief in Jesus Christ and the Church. Are there not some indications or suggestions in the Bible itself concerning its divine character?

5 How can you be absolutely certain that the Bible is the Word of God?

6 Can the Bible state or insinuate anything that is erroneous?

7 What practical conclusions follow logically from the above questions?

How to Study and Meditate on the Bible.

1. Starting point, a *fact:* our modern eagerness to devour all sorts of books, magazines, newspapers. The press governs a man's opinions and life. By way of contrast, note the reluctance of Christians to read the Bible. Modern man is starving for the words of men, which are often empty, disappointing, misleading, but

he disdains the substantial, nourishing, infallible word of God. From this strange anomaly there follows the progressive secularization of thought and of life, for as we think, so we live; and as we read, so we think. There is need in this matter for a Christian reaction—that is, we should read and meditate on the Holy Scriptures.

2. The Bible is filled with riches waiting to be discovered.

a) In it we find *life-giving doctrine* both dogmatic and moral, and learn of God's attitude towards us. The first chapters of Genesis, for example, open up to us a world-view of man at the peak of earthly beings; of man as the viceroy of creation, as the vicar of God; of man both very important and, in comparison with God, a nothing. From the story of Eden we can learn the theology of sin, temptation, repentance, etc.

b) The Bible sets before our eyes a *history* which is a light to live by: it divulges the secret of man's history, the divine drama which begins with "paradisal unity," goes on through the "diabolical separation," and must return to "heavenly achievement." It is the history of our ancestors, for, as Pius XI once said, "spiritually we are all Semites."

c) It furnishes us with some incomparable expressions for our prayers, which are the very breath of our soul. The Missal we use is a biblical anthology.

3. But this substantial bread, like material bread, is won only by the sweat of our brow, by serious study:

a) *Assiduous study.*

"You will acquire a taste for this divine banquet. Every day you will sit down to it, not for long hours at a time—I do not ask this—but for a few moments in the morning, when the burdens of the preceding day will have been lifted from your heart by sleep, and those of the new day have not yet weighed down your spirit. You will make this rising in the word of God a well-beloved dawn of all your labor. . . . The morning is the world's awakening; let it be yours also. Consecrate some of the virginal dawn to meditation on that more splendid and purer dawn which is the word of God. The one is the light of your eyes; the other, of your heart. May they both shine upon you at the same time so that your whole life may be lightsome."[8]

b) *As complete a study as possible.*

Let us consider **all** of the words, for "whatever things have been written, have been written for our instruction" (Rom 15:4). Let us seek out their full meaning, confident that the Scriptures of which God is the author conceal inexhaustible treasures. Let us be eager to profit from them in every possible way. We should not seek the "ascetical point of view," or the "theological point of view," or the "historical point of view." In order to arrive at a full understanding of the text we should use any of the means at our disposal, reading commentaries, listening to explanations spontaneously given or deliberately sought after.

c) *An orderly study.*

The different books of the Bible, each of which possesses its own special genius, its own special meaning for us, should not be taken up by whim or chance or read haphazardly. So important and divine a work demands our serious attention; it should be read according to an intelligent plan.[9]

d) *A study made savorous by meditation.*

Prayer alone brings the reader into contact with the Author of the Bible, and effects that affinity of spirit necessary for its full understanding. The reading of the Scriptures does not produce its effect *ex opere operato*. But if the text of the Scriptures is received with faith and humility and meditated on prayerfully, with the intention of finding what is useful in it rather than of satisfying one's curiosity about it, little by little it will transform the soul of the Christian. This is the way the Church traditionally uses and studies the Bible.[10]

277

II.   Origin of the World—Science and the Bible

Points for Discussion

1   Is the first page of the Bible to be looked upon as a chapter in a textbook of natural science? In describing the origin of the universe, does the Bible pursue a scientific goal?

2   Does the Bible speak conclusively about those facts which are taken up in textbooks on natural science? Does the Bible solve problems which are proper to science?

3   Can the Bible be in conflict with science when both treat of the same questions? Are there statements in the first chapters of the Bible which contradict the conclusions stated in the science textbooks?

4   What is meant by saying that the human authors of the Bible express themselves "according to what appears to the senses" or according to the "scientific opinions of their times?" In using such manners of expression, does the Bible make "scientific errors?" How do we express ourselves in such matters?

5   Have you heard of Evolution? What do scientists think of it? Philosophers? Theologians?

6   Does the Bible approve or condemn the transformation of species? What are some of the ways in which we might understand the evolution of matter and of life?

7   What does the Bible have to say about the origin of matter and of life?

8 To what extent may a Christian accept the theory of evolution?

III. Origin of Man according to the Bible and Science[11]

*Points for Discussion and
Outline of Discussion.*

1 When did man appear on earth? This question may be proposed in two ways:

a) How much time elapsed between the formation of the earth and the appearance of man? According to the Bible, man came on the scene on the sixth day. But as the framework of six days is artificial and symbolical (cf ch 2), the Bible does not offer a precise answer here. How could it? According to science, millions and millions of years may have passed between the formation of the earth and man's appearance on it. This does not contradict the Bible. Why not?

b) What length of time separates us from our first ancestors? According to the Bible, it is impossible to go back through the ages with any degree of certainty, for the genealogies listed in the sacred text are artificial and intentionally incomplete. Profane history and paleontology propose different and very high estimates, ranging from 30,000 to 60,000, or 100,000 to 600,000 years.

2 **Where** did man first appear? The Bible permits us to suppose that man appeared not far from the earthly paradise. But where locate the garden of Eden? As to this there are two opinions among Catholic interpreters:

a) Up to the beginning of this century, all of the exegetes, and even now a respectable number of writers, held that the description of Eden is objective and strictly historical. Because of the details, and especially because of the mention made of the Tigris and the Euphrates rivers, they think it probable that the cradle of the human race should be located near the Persian Gulf.

b) Other exegetes, and their number is steadily increasing, believe that the description of the site of paradise is above all else an ideal or popular one, aimed at conjuring up some idea of man's primitive happiness in a concrete way and in accordance with the ideas of the times. We are free to choose either of these two *opinions*.

Science teaches that at the begining of the Quaternary Period man already existed in China, Africa, Central Europe. But where did he come from? It is a mystery. On this point science cannot at present satisfy our curiosity.

3 **How** did man appear? Two texts in the Bible deal with this point:

a) "God (Elohim) said: Let us make mankind in our image . . ." (Gen 1:26-27).

b) "Then the Lord God (Yahweh Elohim) formed man out of the dust of ground and breathed into his nostrils the breath of life, and man became a living being" (Gen 2:7).

But:

(1) The first text merely affirms the fact that man was formed by God, and says nothing about the manner in which this was done.

(2) The second text seems to be more detailed; yet in it there are some things which are not to be taken in a strict sense: God did not make a figure of clay as a potter does, and he did not breathe a material breath from his lungs. The author especially wished to point out that the whole man (body and soul) owes his existence to a special divine intervention. How was this carried out? As regards man's body we may hold diverse opinions, but there can be no doubt that his soul was created by God.

(3) (a) The body of man with all its parts *could* have been created by God instantaneously.

(b) The body of man *could* have been produced from the slime of the earth.

(c) The body of man *could* have been prepared over many centuries by a long, slow evolution. God would have directed such an evolution until that day, appointed in his infinite wisdom, when a new element would be bestowed on the body he had prepared through secondary causes — the spiritual soul whereby man is truly man.

4 Does the Bible teach us the precise manner in which the woman was made? Actually, the Bible does contain a special account of the origin of the woman (Gen 2:21 f):

(a) We will grant that a large part of this account is devoted to the setting: like a skilled surgeon, God first anaesthetizes the patient, putting him to sleep; and then he proceeds with the extraction of the rib, after which he "builds up" the woman.

(b) We ought especially to stress the teaching contained in the narrative: the man and the woman are of the same nature, of the same flesh. "This woman is a man," exclaims Adam. (This was a reaction against the prevalent pagan view according to which a woman was a being of an inferior nature, made to be the slave of the man.) The woman completes the man in marriage (monogamy and indissolubility of the conjugal union).

(c) Does this not imply that the woman was derived physically from the first man? In its most obvious sense the text favors the traditional interpretation, but modern theologians and exegetes, appealing to the encyclical "On the Promotion of Biblical Studies" (*Divino Afflante Spiritu*) and the "Letter to Cardinal Suhard," lean towards an interpretation in which symbolism plays a large part. Eve then may be said to come from the first man as a picture is derived from a model. In justification of this view, recourse is had to the theory of "literary forms."

Scientists as a whole accept the theory of evolution as at least the most probable *hypothesis* thus far formulated. Many Catholic scholars hold as we do above, but they would be quick to admit that the **fact** of evolution has not yet been proved.[12]

5 Was there once a single original pair, or more than one? In her exposition of dogma, and especially of the dogma of original sin, the Church always assumes that there was but one single couple at the beginning of the human race. On this point, freedom of discussion is not permitted a child of the Church. Science in its present state does not disprove monogenism, because, being unable to locate the cradle of humanity, it can teach us nothing about the number of the first men. The actual diversity of races can be explained in different ways, particularly by environmental conditions.

IV. The History of the Earthly Paradise

Points for discussion:

1 Does the account of what took place in the earthly paradise resemble history in the classical and modern sense of the word?

2 May we deny *en bloc* all objective value to this very special history?

3 Are we obliged to affirm *en bloc* the historical reality of everything contained in the narrative of the temptation and the fall?

4 What are "the fundamental truths underlying the economy of salvation" that are to be found in the history of human origins?

5 Which elements in the story may possibly not be strictly historical?

6 Is it left to us to decide what is and what is not historical? Has the Church given us any directives on this point?

7 Are the responses of the Biblical Commission opposed to further scientific research? In what spirit should these researches be pursued by scientists and interpreted by the faithful?

IV

In the pulpit the great principle of every preacher ought to be to speak in such a way that he will not shock simple souls; yet at the same time he shall make it clear to the more learned of his listeners that he is aware of their difficulties. As a general rule, disputed topics should not be brought up in sermons preached to an ordinary congregation. One should never use the pulpit for a detailed exposition of the "historico-idealistic" theory, or of the harmony existing between the Bible and science. All the more reason, then, why the pulpit-orator should not speak disparagingly of older interpretations, or pose as the champion of new views.

By all means one should avoid that supercilious attitude which proclaims its own foolishness in words like these: "Hitherto you were taught that the world was really created in six days or six periods . . . that the serpent was a real animal . . . but your teachers did not understand . . ."

We must teach the great truths *positively:* the dogma of creation; the divine attributes; God's omnipotence and his wisdom and goodness toward men. We should aim at arousing feelings of admiration and gratitude in the hearts of our congregation. In describing the origin of the universe and of man we should not be afraid to make use of the traditional terminology, but at the same time we should in our exposition make it clear to those acquainted with modern problems that we are aware of them too.

V

Objections:

1 *"Religion is changing."*

No! Religion does not change, but only the manner in which it is presented. Modern exegesis respects all the truths of the faith, and also the certain conclusions of theology. Among these we may single out: the creation of the universe by God in the beginning of time, the special intervention of the Creator in the production of man, the unity of the human race, the elevation of our first parents to the supernatural state, their preternatural privileges, their trial and disobedience at the instigation of the evil spirit, the fall of the human race, the promise of a Redeemer. But these facts of dogmatic import are hidden under a folklorish covering and are related against the background of a dramatic setting invented by the author. Thus, the historico-idealistic explanation does not overstep the limits of the most rigid orthodoxy, even though it rejects the realistic presentation which was commonly accepted at the beginning of the century.

2 *"By your own admission you sacrifice tradition."*

We must answer this with a distinction: are we sacrificing a divine tradition obliging in faith? No. A traditional and human opinion? Yes.[13]

Even when they propose their new theories, modern exegetes are not lacking in respect for the Fathers, nor should they rashly be judged presumptuous. For "not a few things, especially in matters pertaining to history, were scarcely at all or not fully explained by the commentators of the past ages, since they lacked almost all the information which was needed for their clearer exposition. How difficult for the Fathers themselves—and indeed wellnigh unintelligible—were certain passages, is shown among other things, by the oft-repeated efforts of many of them to explain the first chapters of Genesis."[14]

It is undeniable that our age, by the grace of God, "possesses new means and aids to exegesis." The nature and effects of biblical inspiration and the psychology of the sacred authors have been investigated more thoroughly, and we have explored the "literary forms," compared the Bible with the literatures of its neighbors. We have profited by the certain conclusions of the sciences regarding the antiquity of man, and given due consideration to the latest trends in the biological sciences.

What has been called fluctuation in theology and change in exegesis is actually genuine progress. The uninstructed often confuse the infallibility of the Church with omniscience; they profess a kind of "immobility" and are opposed to all change. Infallibility does not, of course, apply to all acts of the teaching Church, but only to those—and they are relatively few—in which the Church exercises her plenary authority. As to the literal or more or less symbolical interpretation of the first chapters of Genesis, the Church has never entirely committed herself. That there has been progress in the understanding of her dogma and of biblical exegesis is a matter of record.

There are undoubtedly statements in the Bible which exclude *a priori* every interpretation which differs from the traditional exegesis. Thus, it will always be true that the Scriptures teach the essential superiority of man and woman over the animal, the ideal happiness offered to our first parents, the universal fall caused by sin. But aside from those passages whose explanations are unchangeable, how many others are there which do admit of new versions! The Fathers, theologians and exegetes held the obvious meaning of the text as long as they had no reason for doubting its proper meaning. But the possibility of less rigid explanations is not excluded, and this is the case as regards the cosmogony of the first chapter. Our present better understanding of "literary forms" permits us to question the objectivity of the description of paradise, and of the realistic interpretation of the origin of the man and of the woman.

3 *"Your exegesis has become infected with the evolutionary ideas now so much in vogue."*

The modern sciences have indeed stimulated the exegetes and they should keep the theologians also on their toes. We thus benefit by an invaluable "mutual enlightenment." But we disavow any taking of sides, either for or against evolutionary ideas; we maintain that as far as evolution is concerned the Bible is neutral.

4 *"Is it not impertinent to dissect a historical work like Genesis, under pretext of separating what is substantially historical from the literary fiction?"*

The impertinence, rather, would be to affirm or to deny *categorically* the historicity of the first chapters

288

of Genesis. The "all or nothing" idea shows that the objector has not grasped the original character of the history of beginnings and that he wrongly identifies the ancient literary forms with those of Graeco-Roman and modern literature.

5 *"Arbitrary dismemberment!"*

The modern explanation does, it is true, run the risk of giving such an impression to the uninitiated, and exegetes who have wholeheartedly dedicated themselves to this arduous task have had to suffer much for their devotion. In replying to objections raised against the Bible, it is difficult to give complete answers to those who are ill-prepared for them. "The serious apologist, who has regard both for the text and for his audience, will give a sound answer to the popular objections drawn from the exploits of Samson, or the adventures of Jonas, or the marvelous history of Tobias; but his answer unfortunately will not be within the grasp of all his hearers. His explanations will seem to be subtle, violent and arbitrary, because they do not understand the complexity of the questions raised by the difficulty."[15]

We will, however, readily grant that the danger of abitrary explanations is a real danger. To be convinced of this one has only to leaf through the attempts at literary analysis to which the narratives of paradise and of the Fall have given rise. With the help of a few meagre details, one author will reconstruct the oral tradition underlying the Genesis narrative; another will track down two or more written documents lying at the base of the biblical text; a third will smell out interpolations or redactional glosses; in short, more solutions than the differences of the text demand. When, however, authors formed in different disciplines and of diverse religious views arrive independently at the same conclusion, it would be unfair to accuse them all of arbitrariness or of prejudice.

6 *"What you say smells strongly of Modernism!"*

This is pure calumny! Modernism retained the traditional formulas but emptied them of their substance, whereas our historico-idealistic interpretation never loses sight of the exigencies of Catholic dogma. In its most critical phase, Modernism likened biblical traditions to the Babylonian myths; our progressive exegesis ventures to take the background of mythological documents into account without succumbing to the temptation of reducing the Bible to the level of mythology. Finally, we modern exegetes manifest our absolute deference to the authority of the Church, and no one would ever attribute such an attitude to Modernism. Modernists like Loisy admittedly did stir things up, but Loisy was not the first heretic to have been an occasion for a development in the sacred sciences.

7 *"A dangerous method! Applied to the history of Israel or to the gospel narrative, it would cause the very foundations of religion to vanish into thin air."*

It is true that this method presents some danger, but this merely points up the fact that it should be handled with care. As for its application to the history of Israel or to the gospel accounts, e g, to the infancy-gospel, this cannot—in virtue of the very principles of the method itself—be done; biblical history as a whole, and the gospel history in particular, belong to different literary forms than those of the first chapters of Genesis. There are many ways of writing history.

8 *"Do you not realize how difficult it is to draw a line between the historical minimum which is to be preserved and what is only its vehicle and means of expression?"*

This separation is indeed a delicate operation. But to assist us we have at our disposal, among other things, the comparative method, and we allow ourselves to be guided by the directives of the Church's Teaching Authority.

9 *"Your method is strangely similar to the method which pagan philosophers once applied to the poems of Homer and Hesiod, and in general to mythological legends, for the purpose of making them acceptable* *to cultured minds. This is an insidious sort of rationalism!"*

The method here alluded to was inaugurated in the 6th century before Christ by Theagenes of Rhegium, and aimed at making literary works and legends serve both philosophy and morality; it involved a constant turning toward allegory. Among the Alexandrian Jews, who adopted it in their exegesis, Philo was its great exponent. Origen also carried it too far. To see how different this method and ours is, one has only to read Philo's "Allegorical Commentary on the Holy Laws, according to the Work of the Six Days." Historico-idealistic exegesis renounces allegory, but it allows for the large part the literary cloak plays in the presentation of the facts of "primordial history." Such a system cannot be said to be an insidious sort of rationalism, since it insists on the fact that there is a supernatural intervention at the origin of humanity.

10 *"The dissemination of such theories will scandalize the faithful."*

There need be no scandal, nor need we risk shaking the faith of the unlettered, if in the classroom and in the pulpit we observe the rules of prudence which we have stated above. An explanation may very well be the true one and yet is not to be taught indiscriminately.

VI

Finis libri, sed non finis quaerendi! "The end of the book—but not the end of our search!" These words of Saint Bernard aptly express our state of mind as we bring this book to a close. An enormous amount of work remains to be done before we can "see more clearly into the true nature of certain narrations of the first chapters of Genesis. . . . Meanwhile we must practice that patience which is living prudence and wisdom."[16]

In the meantime let all who read these pages recall the wise advice given by Saint Ignatius of Loyola at the beginning of his *Spiritual Exercises:* "It must be taken for granted that a good Christian will be quicker to put a charitable interpretation on another's words than to condemn them as false. If he cannot interpret another's words in an orthodox sense, he should ask the speaker what he means by them. If then he proves to be wrong, he should be corrected with charity. If this is insufficient, all proper means should be employed so that his words may be given a correct meaning, and he himself may be saved."

NOTES

1 J Guitton, *Le Développement des Idées dans l'Ancien Testament,* 36.

2 H Junker, *op cit,* p 7.

3 Several more or less successful attempts have been made in French in recent years; the task remains to be done in English.

4 J Colomb, *op cit,* 39.

5 Letter of Fr. Vosté to Cardinal Suhard, cf *H P R,* 48 (1948), 573b.

6 Cf the excellent *Cours d'Histoire Sainte,* edited by the Sisters of Vorselaar, and published under the direction of Canon Coppens.

7 *Humani Generis,* # 37.

8 Père Lacordaire, OP, *Letters to a Young Man,* Second Letter.

9 Cf H Poelman, *How to Read the Bible* (Kenedy, 1953).

10 A recent instruction of the Biblical Commission, May 13, 1950 (*A A S* 9 [1950], 498-499), strongly emphasizes the importance of daily reading of the Sacred Scriptures for priests, and outlines the method to be used in this precious exercise.

11 The review *Gregorianum* 29 (1948) has devoted a special number to reports on the origin of man which were presented during the *Semaine Théologique* in Rome Sept 20-25, 1948.

12 See the explanation just above, p 291.

PRACTICAL APPLICATIONS

13 At the Tenth Biblical Week, held at the Pontifical Institute in Rome on Sept 27-Oct 1, 1948, Father Bea, SJ, treated the question of transformism from the exegetical point of view. In the discussion which followed his paper, the patristic argument favoring the traditional position was raised in objection: "If the consensus of the Fathers and of Tradition is invalid in this question, then that is the end of every argument drawn from Tradition and the consent of the Fathers." Father Bea replied, "This consensus of the Fathers cannot be considered as the authentic *interpretation* of the text, as the Fathers here merely *repeat* what the text says, having no doubts as to the literal understanding of the biblical narrative." (*Verbum Domini* [1948] 326.)

14 Pius XII, *Divino Afflante Spiritu*, # 31.

15 "Inspiration et Inerrance," *D A*, 754.

16 Letter of Father Vosté to Cardinal Suhard, *loc cit*, 574.

INDEX OF BIBLICAL TEXTS

INDEX OF BIBLICAL TEXTS

297

INDEX OF BIBLICAL TEXTS

INDEX OF BIBLICAL TEXTS

INDEX OF BIBLICAL TEXTS

INDEX OF BIBLICAL TEXTS

INDEX OF AUTHORS CITED

INDEX OF AUTHORS CITED